PANDEMIC 2020

When the Abnormal Became the New Normal
As Viewed from a Mental Health Perspective

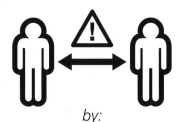

by:
Cheryl Powell
Cover Credit to Tanya Powell

...and, "Whatever Happened to All the Toilet Paper?"

DORRANCE
PUBLISHING CO
EST. 1920
PITTSBURGH, PENNSYLVANIA 15238

The contents of this work, including, but not limited to, the accuracy of events, people, and places depicted; opinions expressed; permission to use previously published materials included; and any advice given or actions advocated are solely the responsibility of the author, who assumes all liability for said work and indemnifies the publisher against any claims stemming from publication of the work.

Dorrance Publishing Co
585 Alpha Drive
Pittsburgh, PA 15238

Visit our website at www.dorrancebookstore.com

ISBN: 978-1-6491-3473-8
eISBN: 978-1-6491-3822-4

To my son Mark,

his wife Joanne,

my grandson Nathan,

and also to my daughter Tanya.

To Mia and Missie.

And to friends, and family.

You are loved and appreciated.

May you stay forever safe and well.

This book is also dedicated to my colleagues and the front-line workers battling this pandemic, my "essential" companions who kept their families and communities across the world as safe as was humanly possible during the 2020 PANDEMIC – some at the expense of their lives.

I also dedicate this to the White House Press Office, the Coronavirus Task Force and teams, WHO, CDC, Senate and Congress, and also to the various governors who helped to keep us informed in a tireless manner never seen before in American history, at least up until the end of this first account, Part I, which concludes with May 17, The End of the Beginning, heralding what unknown comes next in Part II.

Also, with much thanks to the media who also kept us informed, such as FOX News, CNN, MSNBC, ABC, CBS, NBC, BBC, 7-News, NECN, The New York Times, The Washington Post, The Wall Street Journal, The Cape Cod Times, and countless others across the nation and worldwide.

Finally, I dedicate this account to those lives lost, and with many sympathies to their families and loved ones.

After costs, it is my intention to share any profits from this account to help build supplies for future crises in the hope of saving lives by being better prepared.

HYSTERIA: a psychological disorder whose symptoms include conversion of psychological stress into physical symptoms, selective amnesia, shallow volatile emotions, and overdramatic or attention-seeking behavior. The term has a controversial history, as it was formerly regarded as a disease specific to women.

VIRUS: an infective agent that typically consists of a nucleic acid molecule in a protein coat, is too small to be seen by light microscopy, and is able to multiply only within the living cells of a host.

RESILIENCE: the capability of a strained body to recover its size and shape after deformation caused especially by compressive stress; an ability to recover from or adjust easily to misfortune or change

HERD IMMUNITY: an epidemiological concept that describes the state where a population – usually of people – is sufficiently immune to a disease that the infection will not spread within that group. In other words, enough people have become immune, usually through vaccination or natural immunity – that the people who are vulnerable are better protected.

SOCIAL DISTANCING: or physical distancing; a set of non-pharmaceutical interventions or measures taken to prevent the spread of a contagious disease by maintaining a physical distance between people and reducing the number of times people come into close contact with each other.

PANDEMIC: adjective (of a disease) prevalent over a whole country or the world.

EPIDEMIC: a widespread occurrence of an infectious disease in a community at a particular time.

PROLOGUE

It is hard to believe that the most powerful country in the world could be brought to its knees, indeed collapsing the entire world to its knees - by something so small and fragile that it cannot even be seen, BUT IT DID HAPPEN... serving as a bitter warning to future generations to be prepared.

So, who am I, and why am I writing this account? Me – I am nobody. Then again, I am everybody. I am my patients. I am you. Like you, I am a member of this new world into which we have all been shoved by COVID-19, a new social order, a humbling, a new world – that will survive.

My first career was as a nurse working in a cancer research hospital in the mid-western United States. This was short-lived, as I married and moved to England where there was no reciprocity for American nurses. I then worked as a trainee bank assistant manager, leaving that profession after I had my two children, devoting the next sixteen years to building my career as a journalist, working my way up to Senior Editor and Editorial Manager of a small American newspaper based in the UK, splitting my time between both America and England, also living for seven months in Malaysia and Singapore, working on international travel and connections and having had the honor to visit nearly a hundred countries as a travel column courtesy.

Returning to America in 1998, I later obtained my Master's degree in mental health, and I have been working for the past 11 years as a professional clinician in a challenging field to help my patients collect and reconnect the puzzle pieces of their lives back together. Some have lost their children, spouse, parents, other loved ones, while others are plagued by voices and hallucinations. Most have simply become overwhelmed with life events and need an empathetic ear and emotional shoulder to cry on, a safe place to voice their concerns, while others have endured tragic traumatic events where they need help moving beyond the trauma.

And then we received an unwelcomed visit by a virus, resulting in the world population suddenly suffering to some degree from PTSD. However, like those

I treat, we can and the human race will survive this, and it is my firm belief that we, as a species, can emerge stronger and more resilient. We need to discard our former complacency and work together because this virus, or something very similar, will come back again, and we need to be prepared. Meanwhile, we are all in this together.

"We have always held to the hope, the belief, the conviction that there is a better life, a better world, beyond the horizon."
        – Franklin Delano Roosevelt (January 30, 1882 – April 12, 1945)

As President of the United States from 1933-1945, FDR won a record four presidential elections, implemented his New Deal in response to the worst economic crisis in US history, previously. Roosevelt contracted a paralytic illness, believed at the time to be polio, in 1921, after which his legs became permanently paralyzed. Poliomyelitis is a virus that spreads from person to person. He died roughly five months before the end of WWII, which ravaged most of his third and fourth terms as President of the United States.

CHAPTER 1
What Came Before

It must have been back in October or November of 2019 when I was first confronted with this event. Perhaps I simply did not recognize it. As a practicing mental health professional with a large caseload, I hear all sorts of stories and accounts. I treat all ages, and all diagnoses, which means that my days are filled with accounts of family discourse, disagreeable or dysfunctional children, trauma reactions due to emotional or physical abuse that span the entire gambit from being shouted at to miracle survivals after multiple shootings, stabbings, strangulations, poisoning, or similar. Some of my patients have been coming to me for years for nothing more than a check-in and an opportunity for an emotional vent. Others come because it's a requirement to have therapy for their med-provider to prescribe, to maintain their parole, or to be allowed back in their home as ordered by their companions and families. I often even hear from neighbors and friends who know what I do for a living, who occasionally visit for a coffee and a therapeutic chat. I thought I had heard it all.

That is – until the Autumn of 2019 when two individuals, independently and neither without any known knowledge of the other, both who seemed relatively healthy, professional, and with no known underlying concerns, contacted me to explore their adamant sense of dread; they instinctively knew that something horrible was approaching, very soon, that they were going to die, and that they would be one of many.

As a practitioner, I urged an exploration of this sense of dread. Where did it come from? Was there a reason such as recent deaths in their family or of someone close? Had they recently overcome an illness, or did they have an ongoing life-threatening illness of which I had previously been unaware? We also explored the natural progression of life and how it is "normal" as one ages to begin looking back on their lives and accomplishments, what was achieved, regrets, missed opportunities, things they wanted to change, what was ahead of them. We discussed the theory of psychological development posed by the

Cheryl Powell

German-American psychologist and psychoanalyst Erik Erikson. Since these two individuals were in their early 50s and early 60s, they respectively fell within Erikson's stages of "Generativity vs. Stagnation" and "Integrity vs. Despair," the first pertaining to the time of life where you identify with your life's work and begin contributing to the next generation, the latter where the life-task is to reflect on your life and view it with a sense of satisfaction, or a sense of failure. Generally, one can help an individual, whether it be a friend, colleague, or patient, through an educated exploration and discussion, reframing and normalizing, but such was not the case with these two separate individuals. One was a former colleague whom I had known for years, and the other a friend I had known for several months. I respected them both and believed them to be level-headed, yet this topic had never been mentioned previously. Nevertheless, both were adamant. Something was going to happen! And it was going to happen soon!

It is known that animals have keen senses that help them to avoid predators, or even to locate their prey, and it is believed that many animals can sense pending disasters. When the 2005 tsunami hit Sri Lanka, it was reported that elephants were seen running away, and bats flew off before the massive waves could even be seen approaching from the distance. Of course, earthquakes bring with them vibrational changes, and storms cause electromagnetic changes in the atmosphere. How many times have we heard stories of cats running away to find a place to die peacefully, indicating that they are more attuned to their bodies and environment, able to detect signs associated with pending death?

In April of 2016, US researcher and geophysicist, Joe Kirschvink from the California Institute of Technology, presented initial results from his studies in sixth sense for humans, claiming that humans have functioning magnetoreceptors. One of his hypotheses was that Earth's magnetic field could trigger reactions in proteins called cryptochromes that are found in the retinas of birds, dogs, and humans. The other hypothesis is that there are iron-building magnetite crystals, found in various organs that become magnetized. It is also thought that dogs use Earth's magnetic fields to regulate their bowel and bladder behavior. Did you ever wonder why a dog deliberates over where to relieve

2

itself? Is it not simply to delay being taken back home or inside? I certainly believed that of my wonderful yellow Labrador, Mia, where I had previously always translated her rather forlorn look at me whilst making a biological deposit on the grass as a, "Do I have to go back inside now?" However, a two-year study of 70 dogs from 37 different breeds was conducted by the Czech University of Life Sciences, publishing their results in 2013 in the *Frontiers of Zoology*. Based on 1,893 observations of defecation, and 5,582 observations of urination, their findings were that, "Dogs preferred to excrete with their body being aligned along a North-South axis," with respect to Earth's magnetic field. Terrific - dogs have a North-South pooping axis.

Also, it would seem that dogs have a sense of smell that is 10,000 to 100,000 times more sensitive than humans, having up to 300 million scent detectors as opposed to roughly 6 million detectors in humans, which is undoubtedly why there are studies to train dogs to detect cancer in humans. More recently, the University of Pennsylvania's School of Veterinary Medicine commenced research to see if the dog's keen sense of smell could be harnessed to identify COVID-19 infection in asymptomatic humans. In a recent *Live Science* publication, author Mindy Weisberger quotes Cynthia Otto, Director of Penn Vet's Working Dog Center, as explaining that, cells can produce volatile organic compounds that have distinctive odors that are present, "in human blood, saliva, urine or breath."

There are numerous studies regarding animal behavior. As humans, we no longer need to hunt for our food, aside from seeking out the correct aisle in a supermarket. Neither do we need to arm ourselves for protection when leaving our homes due to possible natural dangers in the environment such as wild animals - also in search of a tasty meal. For the most part, we enjoy the luxury of no longer finding ourselves as the prey, so we rely on the five main senses of touch, sight, hearing, smell, and taste. But what about our sixth sense that we often hear about in a good book or a new movie? I could not help but wonder if there was something innate, possibly some sense lying deeper within the human species, being revealed in the fears of pending danger that were being relayed to me. These two individuals had no doubt in their minds. Something was coming!

3

Odder still was that a part of me shared their uneasiness, and while they were speaking my mind wandered to my basement where, commencing in September of 2019, I began a storage area for emergencies that consisted of canned foods, pastas, staples, constructing twelve shelves with newly purchased storage jars for dry goods, installing a generator, and arranging another storage area in the garage for extra batteries, flashlights and lanterns. The mental health practitioner in me wanted to help these two individuals to ease their fears. The human being in me shared their trepidation.

"I shall not commit the fashionable stupidity of regarding everything I cannot explain as a fraud."
  – Carl Jung, psychiatrist, delivered in 1919 during the Spanish Flu Pandemic while addressing the Society for Psychical Research in England

CHAPTER 2
The Purpose

This is an account not only as a participant in this horrible and currently ongoing event based on all available information at this time in a situation that is constantly changing, but it is also an account of the observed, and experienced, impact of such an adversity on mental health. At present, I intend to write this account in two, possibly three, parts. It will have world information, yet most pertains to how the pandemic unfolds in America. Although all states will be covered, not all will be covered in immense detail, with far more of the states covered more specifically in the next account. This is also a view of the impact on the economy of our nation, the trust of our citizens, colliding with the effect on the mental health of the human race as a whole. I extend this to the "human race" because the simple fact is that this event, by its very nature, will forever change our world. It will never be the same. However, there is also another blaringly obvious observance that, whether for better or worse, we all have a part in this crisis. The human race will definitely survive, yet what we do now will determine the shape of tomorrow - our "new normal."

This first account tries to provide a background of what was happening before the virus struck, what happened in the beginning, and by the end of the beginning. Unlike many who believe that because things are looking brighter with the summer months approaching, that we are therefore finished with what is frequently referred to as "the beast," it is my belief that this is only the beginning and that the beast is not quite finished with inflicting its damage. How we continue to deal with it will determine the fate of the virus, and ourselves. What legacy, truths, and incredibly important lessons will we leave behind for our children and our children's children? What perspective will we bequeath to them? Will we be proud of the legacy we leave behind, or ashamed? You see, this is also an account for my family. I grew up feeling relatively safe in America. My family had left me with much information of the past, the wars, verbal legacies, ancestors, but nothing from past pandemics. There is nothing available to tell me how they survived and what they had learned from what happened then so that I might apply it now. Therefore, I am writing this account so that my family will know how I survived, or perhaps why I did not survive. That will be dictated not only by the virus that is hungry for a host, but also dictated by what I do, and what is done by the human race.

I also invite feedback on what I write, information on what happened where you live, special stories, even corrections, and photos, which I intend to include in updates and the next account. What have we learned?

As for patients, I must respect their privacy. Therefore, no specific patients will be named or otherwise identified, and some information may be altered so that none can glean any possible identities, or identify themselves, although I do intend to invite patients and others to contribute to subsequent accounts if they so desire, as this is not just my account. This is happening to everyone, and all are important.

As for perspective, far too many say that, "The virus may come back in the autumn." The truth is that IT HASN'T LEFT YET.

PERSPECTIVE

"Yes, I remember the barbed wire and the guard towers and the machine guns, but they became part of my normal landscape. What would be abnormal in normal times became my normality in camp."

– George Takei

CHAPTER 3
So, What Happened:
(as far as we know at this stage in the crisis)

History will probably show that this all began, at least according to current, and shifting thinking, when a little known 33-year-old Chinese doctor named Li Wenliang, an ophthalmologist working at the Wuhan (a city roughly 700 miles south of Beijing) Central Hospital in China, sent a warning to his fellow medics on December 30, 2019, about a new virus that he thought looked like the SARS virus that had led to a global epidemic in 2003.

On December 31, 2019, the Chinese health officials informed the World Health Organization (WHO) that they had a cluster of 41 patients suffering with a mysterious pneumonia, where most were connected to the Huanan Seafood Wholesale Market in Wuhan, China. It is noted that, according to Wuhan Municipal Health, those cases occurred between December 12-29.

The Dow Jones closed at 29,379.77 on December 31, 2019.
The FTSE closed at 7,542 on December 31, 2019.

Whilst all this was happening, American news continued to focus heavily on the heated impeachment proceedings, paying relatively little attention to the financial, emotional, and health crisis that was threatening to storm across the country in the incredibly near future, the silent enemy that was lurking on our doorstep.

The news headlines from the New York Times on January 1 included articles on protesters attacking the US Embassy in Iraq, chanting, "Death to America," New Year's pictures, and how the "Science Panel Staffed with Trump Appointees Says E.P.A. Rollbacks Lack Scientific Rigor." *The Times* was little different than other major papers, who focused their attentions firmly on the impeachment process, the squabbling between the Democratic and Republican parties, and general discourse thriving in our nation's capital. No one can really blame the media. They need ratings and advertising. It is their bread and butter. There seemed to be little information coming out of China, and we had just entered an election year. Nobody really believed the President would be impeached. Even the least observant seemed to believe that this was about discrediting President Trump as the Republican candidate for the 2020 race, hearing not so much about deaths beyond our shores, but more about impeachment and the various Democratic candidates.

Also on January 1, the Huanan Seafood Market was closed by the Chinese health authorities. Two days later, Dr. Li Wenliang was summoned by the Wuhan police and admonished for "making false comments on the internet." He was accused of being one of eight "rumor mongers".

January 5 saw the announcement by China that the unknown pneumonia cases were not SARS or MERS, and on January 7, the Chinese authorities confirmed that they had a new novel coronavirus, which was initially identified by the WHO as 2019-nCOV. It is worth noting that SARS, an acronym for Severe Acute Respiratory Syndrome, was also first seen in Asia in 2003 and was responsible for an excess of 700 deaths. MERS, standing for Middle East Respiratory Syndrome, was first seen in 2012 in the Middle East, as the name suggests, and was responsible for over 800 deaths. Both were coronaviruses.

Doctor Li Wenliang posted on January 10 that he had started coughing, having a fever the next day. He entered the hospital two days later. It is worth noting that Li's parents also fell ill, yet recovered.

The first death was revealed by the Wuhan Municipal Health Commission on January 11, 2020. The victim was identified as a 61-year-old man who had allegedly been exposed to the virus at the seafood market, dying on January 9 from respiratory failure.

On January 13, the first death was recorded in Bangkok, the capitol of Thailand, after a forensic practitioner contracted the disease after working with a dead infected body. Often regarded as the "Last Responders," forensic pathologists were thought to have a lower chance of becoming infected with COVID-19, due to it being primarily spread through respiratory droplets emitted through coughing, sneezing, or even talking. However, the death in Thailand was proof that everyone was at risk.

By January 20, China reported 139 cases, and a third death. This day also witnessed the WHO's first situation report, confirming other cases in Thailand, South Korea, and Japan. In addition, the first case in the United States was also reported on January 20 in a 35-year-old man who had traveled from China to Snohomish County in Washington State on the northwestern coast of America on January 15. nCOV had arrived in America. In reality, it is worth noting that, at the time of writing this account, there is a suspicion in the United States that the virus may have arrived earlier, or that there are two different strains. This is currently under investigation in this rapidly changing crisis.

Also on January 20, Dr. Anthony Fauci, Director of the National Institute of Allergy and Infectious Disease, announced that, "The NIH (National Institutes of Health) is in the process of taking the first steps towards the development of a vaccine." He also cautioned that it would take a few months until the first phase of the clinical tests might commence, and possibly more than a year before a vaccine was available.

Meanwhile, news headlines in the United States on January 20, 2020, spoke of President Trump unveiling his defense against the impeachment charges, two Honolulu officers being killed in a shooting near Diamond Head, the Kansas City Chiefs defeated the Tennessee Titans 35-24 – earning them their first place in the Super Bowl in roughly half a century, with more news reporting that Puerto Rico's governor had fired several top officials after discovering that they were allegedly stockpiling emergency supplies in a warehouse after Hurricane Maria. Little did they know at the time how much these would soon be needed.

The Dow Jones closed at 29,196.04 on January 21, 2020.
The FTSE closed at 5,853.76 on January 21, 2020.

"I am a firm believer in the people. If given the truth, they can be depended upon to meet any national crisis. The great point is to bring them the real facts."

– Abraham Lincoln, President during America's Civil War, where an estimated 620,000 perished, representing roughly 2 percent of the American population

CHAPTER 4
The Background Upon
Which the Stage is Set

Although this book is non-political, it is worth noting that the stage upon which COVID performed was highly political in the United States. As stated previously, this virus visited the world during an election year in America, and it played out in the political arena. Therefore, it is worth a brief account, according to this humble writer, as to the atmosphere that existed in our country before our un-invited visitor arrived to reap its destruction. Of course, most Americans are all-too aware of where we were "then" as opposed to where we are "now," but what about ten years from now, or twenty, what about the next generation? How will we paint this for our grandchildren, or their children who find themselves con-fronting the next pandemic? Although it may not happen again in our lifetime, history proves that it will most definitely happen again.

In brief and with no party preference...

Even a cursory review of the media indicates that threats to impeach Pres-ident Trump commenced before he was even sworn into office in 2017. An ar-ticle published by Darren Samuelson dated April 17, 2016, seven months before the election itself, was titled: Could Trump Be Impeached Shortly After He Takes Office? Samuelson postulated that, "impeachment is already on the lips of pundits, newspaper editorials, constitutional scholars, and even a few members of Congress..."

As far back as November 14, 2016, T.A. Frank of *Vanity Fair/HIVE* challenged in an article titled: Will Trump Be Impeached?, proposing, "Do a LexisNexis search, and you'll find that 'Trump' and some variant of 'impeach' have already appeared in 37 newspaper headlines." This was only six days after the election!

Controversy plagued his presidency. Almost immediately after winning the election, November 18, 2016, Trump agreed to pay $25 million to settle three lawsuits against Trump University. On December 24, 2016, Trump an-nounced that he was dissolving the Donald J. Trump Foundation, "to avoid even the appearance of any conflict with my role as President." On January 12, 2017, CNN/Politics reported that,

Classified documents presented last week to President Obama and President-elect Trump included allegations that Russian operatives claim to have compromising personal and financial information about Mr. Trump, multiple US officials with direct knowledge of the briefings tell CNN...The FBI is investigating the credibility and accuracy of these allegations...

Nevertheless, and despite the protests of the disgruntled Democratic leaders and those voters who did not vote for him – many who protested on the streets – Donald Trump was sworn in as the 45th President of the United States on January 20, 2017.

Not losing any time, Trump signed an executive order withdrawing America from the Trans-Pacific Partnership on January 23, 2017. Four days later, January 27, 2017, saw the new President signing an executive order to halt all refugee arrivals for 120 days, banning travel to the United States from seven Muslim-majority countries for 90 days.

February and March saw more controversy related to relations with Russia and the 2016 election, resulting in meeting with the Russian President, Vladimir Putin, for the first time on July 7, 2017.

Then August 8, 2017 witnessed what seemed like nuclear threats from North Korea, resulting in President Trump warning that Pyongyang will, "face fire and fury like the world has never seen."

By September of 2017, Trump had announced that his administration would end the DACA program introduced by former President Obama that was intended to protect roughly 800,000 undocumented immigrants who were brought to the United States as children, also allegedly calling on Congress to introduce legislation that would prevent DACA recipients from being deported. Later in the month, September 19, Trump gave a speech at the United Nations General Assembly, referring to the North Korean leader, Kim Jong Un, as "Rocket Man."

September through December 2017 saw more travel bans, and by the Spring of 2018, President Trump had announced a "zero tolerance" policy for illegal border crossings.

By early summer, June 12, Trump had arranged and met with Kim Jong Un for the first time at a summit meeting in Singapore where they signed a four-point statement that outlined their mutual commitment to peace.

Amidst more heated controversy, June 26 witnessed the Supreme Court upholding the Trump Administration's travel ban.

As 2018 drew to a close, President Trump announced on December 19 that the United States had defeated ISIS, followed on December 22 with the US President demanding $5.7 billion to fund a border wall.

On January 16, 2019, former New York City mayor and Trump lawyer, Rudy Giuliani, stated that, "...There is not a single bit of evidence the President of the United States committed the only crime you can commit here, conspiring with the Russians to hack the DNC." Two months later, March 24, 2019, Attorney General William Barr released a letter summarizing the conclusions from Robert Mueller's investigation, clarifying that there was insufficient evidence to establish that members of Trump's campaign engaged in any criminal conspiracy with the Russian government to interfere with the 2016 election...three years earlier.

The New York Times published a report on May 1, 2019, claiming that Trump's attorney, Rudy Giuliani, was investigating allegations related to former Vice President Joe Biden, a potential opponent in the upcoming 2020 Presidential race. This was followed by President Trump holding a rally in Orlando, Florida, on June 18, where he announced the launch of his reelection campaign. The following month, on July 24, Mueller testified before the House Judiciary Committee.

In what seemed to the average American voter and taxpayer like an endless pursuit of President Trump, an unidentified whistleblower reportedly filed a complaint on August 12, 2019, regarding a July 25 call between the President and the Ukrainian President Volodymyr Zelensky. This was followed on September 10 with Adam Schiff, House Intelligence Committee Chairman, reportedly sending a letter to Joseph Maguire, who was the acting Director of National Intelligence, demanding that Maguire share the whistleblower complaint with Congress. On September 18, it was revealed that Schiff reportedly announced that Maguire had agreed to testify, after which House Speaker,

Nancy Pelosi, announced on September 24 the commencement of an impeachment inquiry.

On November 13, 2019, almost exactly one year before the upcoming 2020 election would be held, the public impeachment hearings began, and on December 10, the house Democrats revealed two articles for impeachment, the first for abuse of power, and the second for obstruction of Congress. In response, the House Minority Leader, Kevin McCarthy, stated that, "It is not difficult to defend this President because this President did nothing that is impeachable."

Nevertheless, the two articles were approved on December 13, and the House of Representatives voted along party lines on December 18, 2019, to impeach the 45th President of the United States.

The general feeling in the United States at that time was that the impeachment would never pass the US Senate, and many thought the three-year effort had one goal: to prevent President Donald Trump from serving a second term in the White House, not because of alleged crimes committed, but because such would be the only attack against a President who had grown the US economy over his term of office, but had simultaneously lowered unemployment, according to the Bureau of Labor Statistics (BLS) household survey revealed through the Council of Economic Advisors of May 3, 2019 to, "the lowest unemployment rate since December 1969." Nevertheless, accusations against the President had persisted for three years and dominated much of our headlines, and we seemed to be oblivious to the very real threat that was lurking on the horizon, the very real devastation that was charging towards our shores. Still, there was an election to be held in less than a year.

The year 2020 arrived, and the New Year celebrations had barely grown silent before the US launched an air strike in Iraq, killing the Iranian leader of the Islamic Revolutionary Guards Corps Quds Force, Qasem Soleimani, on January 3. President Trump announced that, "We took action last night to stop a war. We did not take action to start a war," later explaining that Soleimani was planning a major attack against the United States. In retaliation, Iran fired a number of missiles at US troops based in Iraq, with no US or Iraqi lives lost, although it was later also announced that 109 US servicemen had been diagnosed with mild traumatic brain injuries due to the attack.

PANDEMIC 2020

Oddly, and with threats of impeachment returning to dominate the headlines, a trade deal was signed with Chinese leaders on January 15 that included
pledges from Beijing to double its purchases from American farmers, yet still
no real mention was made of the virus sweeping across China, no known hints,
or warnings.

President Trump's proposed impeachment trial commenced the next day,
on January 16, 2020, and on January 21, senators passed a resolution on the
ground rules. The negotiation seemed to end when Senate Majority Leader,
Mitch McConnell (R-KY), stated that he had the votes to move ahead with a resolution, after which the House Speaker, Nancy Pelosi, (D-CA), reportedly delayed transmitting the articles to the Senate for nearly a month.

*"Let us never forget that government is ourselves and not an alien power over
us. The ultimate rulers of our democracy are not a President and senators and
congressmen and government officials, but the voters of this country."*
– Franklin D. Roosevelt

CHAPTER 5
Back in the Lands of COVID

Taiwan confirmed its first case on January 21, identified as a woman in her 50s from southern Taiwan who had returned from working in Wuhan the day before, having been sent directly to the hospital from the airport. Hong Kong also confirmed its first case on January 21. North Korea closed its borders to all foreign travelers on January 22 as China confirmed a caseload of 440, with nine deaths, rising to 17 deaths by the next day when Singapore announced its first case.

A CNN health editorial dated January 23, 2020, written by Michael Nedelman of CNN and titled: World Health Organization - Wuhan Coronavirus is Not Yet a Public Health Emergency of International Concern, reported, "The Wuhan Does not yet Constitute a Public Health Emergency of International Concern, the World Health Organization announced Thursday," quoting that, "Make no mistake. This is an emergency in China, but it has not yet become a global health emergency," WHO Director-General Tedros Adhanom Ghebreyesus said Thursday. "It may yet become one."

Wuhan was placed under quarantine on January 23, with Nepal, Vietnam, France, and Malaysia confirming their first cases on January 24. The next day, January 25, Canada and Australia confirmed their first cases, with Germany identifying their first case on January 27 as the US and Japan prepared to evacuate their citizens from Wuhan and several airlines swiftly suspending their flights to China. The first cases of the virus were announced in Finland and the United Arab Emirates (UAE) on January 29, with Russia closing its borders with China the next day as India announced its first case. Italy made the same announcement on January 31.

An announcement was made by the White House on January 29, 2020, informing the public that a special task force had been formed to monitor and contain the spread of the virus, that the task force had met daily since January 27, and would be, "led by Secretary of Health and Human Services Alex Azar, and is coordinated through the National Security Council," and that other

17

members would include, "Robert O'Brien, Assistant to the President for National Security Affairs, Dr. Robert Redfield, Director of the Centers for Disease Control and Prevention, Dr. Anthony Fauci, Director of the National Institute of Allergy and Infectious Diseases at the National Institutes of Health, Deputy Secretary Stephen Biegun, Department of State, Ken Cuccinelli, Acting Deputy Secretary, Department of Homeland Security, Joel Szabat, Acting Under Secretary for Policy, Department of Transportation, Matthew Pottinger, Assistant to the President and Deputy National Security Advisor, Rob Blair, Assistant to the President and Senior Advisor to the Chief of Staff, Joseph Grogan, Assistant to the President and Director of the Domestic Policy Council, Christopher Liddell, Assistant to the President and Deputy Chief of Staff for Policy Coordination, and Derek Kan, Executive Associate Director, Office of Management and Budget." The White House Briefings were soon to become part of our daily diet.

On January 30, Doctor Li Wenliang posted that, "Today nucleic acid testing came back with a positive result, the dust has settled, finally diagnosed." A Zhejiang medical expert sent to Wuhan, Doctor Yu Chengbo, later informed the Chinese media that, despite the virus infrequently causing severe conditions in younger patients, he believed his colleague, Dr. Li Wenliang, contracted the virus from a glaucoma patient who was a storekeeper at the Huanan Seafood Market, therefore subjecting the whistleblower to a higher viral load.

The WHO declared a global health emergency of international concern on January 30. On the same day, the Philippine Department of Health reported its first case of COVID-19 in a 38-year-old Chinese female national, who was confined in the San Lazaro Hospital in Manila.

President Donald Trump banned foreign nationals from entering the USA on January 31 if they had been in China within the previous two weeks. I will not deny that I was disappointed. Perhaps it was because I used to travel so much, but my first reaction was to question this. I felt very strongly that the President had made the right decision, but why close the front door, whilst leaving the back door and all the windows open? This simply meant that entry had changed to taking indirect flights, stopping off in London, Paris, Italy, or similar. Of course, I told myself, nobody knew exactly what lay before us, and closing everything would have created more political carrots for those quick to ridicule on which to feed while the fabric of our society was beginning to unravel. This was, after all, an election year.

The Dow Jones closed at 28,256.03 on January 31,2020.

The FTSE closed at 7,286 on January 31, 2020.

The Philippines' second case was confirmed on February 2 in a 44-year-old Chinese man who had died a day earlier, representing the Philippines' first recorded death from the virus. By April 19, they had 6,259 confirmed cases, 572 recoveries, and 409 deaths recorded.

On February 3, China's Foreign Ministry spokeswoman, Hua Chunying, chastised US officials for the President's ban on US entry if travelers had been in China within the previous two weeks, stating that, "All it has done could only create and spread fear, which is a bad example." At this stage, China's National Health Commission had confirmed 17,205 cases and 361 deaths. Chinese stock markets plunged.

By February 4, on the same day that the US Food and Drug Administration issued an emergency use for the CDC's diagnostic test, Belgium reported its first case and Japan had 20 identified cases of the virus, which included one individual who had flown to Tokyo on January 17 with his two daughters after spending a day onboard the Diamond Princess cruise ship from January 20-25, seeking medical attention and being diagnosed on January 30. An article in the February 17 *South China Morning Post*, titled: "Coronavirus: 99 more cases on Diamond Princess Cruise Ship in Japan as US Evacuates Citizens," announced that after docking in Yokohama on the completion of its two-week itinerary, medical officials boarded the Diamond Princess and reportedly went room-by-room to check guests, the article claiming that, "The Diamond Princess vessel moored in Yokohama near Tokyo has become the largest cluster of coronavirus cases outside the epicenter in China with 454 cases confirmed." The Diamond Princess, which will be randomly referred to in this account, represented a floating petri dish for what was about to descend on the population and economy of the world as the ship was placed under a quarantine that was originally scheduled to end on February 19.

At this time, it was announced that several cruise lines were enacting new protocols to protect the spread of the virus, such as Princess Cruises and Carnival

Cruises barring guests if they had traveled from or through China during the 14 days prior to their cruise departure date. Royal Caribbean mirrored with a similar reaction, the difference being that they also banned prior travel to Hong Kong, with an extended timing to 15 days beforehand.

Back in the United States, President Trump was acquitted on February 5 following an official inquiry spanning the time from September to November 2019. He was impeached by the US House of Representatives on December 18, 2019, charging him with abuse of power and obstruction of Congress. This represented the third impeachment trial of a US president, preceded by impeachment trials of Andrew Johnson and Bill Clinton. On February 5, 2020 the Senate acquitted Trump on both impeachment articles, with 52 Republican senators voting against the charge of abuse of power, and all fifty-three senators voting against the charge of obstruction of Congress.

More embarrassing to me was the response made after President Trump's State of the Union address the day before, on February 4, where the President spoke of the economy being, "the best it has ever been," and how the, "unemployment rate for women reached the lowest level in almost 70 years," and how, "incomes are raising fast." Once again, and with no party preference, what was any opposition to do against such claims during an election year? The answer seemed to be to respond by publicly tearing up the speech just delivered by the President of the United States. On that occasion, I felt embarrassed to be an American – a nationality and honor of which I have always been proud.

Before proceeding, I choose to reiterate and explain that I am non-political. I make it known that I walked over two miles, in snow, when I reached the age of 18, with the goal of registering to vote. That is my right as an American citizen: one vote for each; one chance to speak; one opportunity to make a difference. I was stunned when I arrived after my long hike and was informed that I would need to declare a party. My response, engraved in memory, was, "Can't I just vote for the right person for the job?" The curt and somewhat bemused reply was, "No. You need to choose one to support." I "chose" Republican, and I do not know why because I have always voted for the candidate I believe to be the best person for the job. I have voted Democrat, Independent, and Republican, and occasionally threatened to vote for Mickey Mouse when I was unsure. This book is no different. It includes political observations because they are very pertinent to this situation. I firmly believe that politics should not be a part of this crisis, but the reality is that politics, sadly, seem to be very much a part of this crisis. Indeed, the virus seems to be the only player that is truly non-political. It does not care. This virus will take anyone. It respects no borders and observes no rules.

The Dow Jones closed at 29,290.85 on February 5, 2020.

The FTSE closed at 7,482.48 on February 5, 2020.

Doctor Li Wenliang died on February 7. The next day, February 8, the first American citizen, a 60-year-old man who lived in Wuhan, died. His family preferred that his name remain undisclosed. February 8 also saw the death toll in China rage to 86 new deaths within 24 hours, bringing their total to 723. By February 9, just one day later, the death toll leaped ahead of the SARS 2002-2003 epidemic to 811 deaths. SARS was first reported in Asia in February of 2003 and according to the World Health Organization (WHO), 8,098 people were infected worldwide, of which 774 died. It is also worth noting that, reportedly, only eight people in America had laboratory evidence of having SARS-CoV, and all of these had traveled to impacted areas.

The President later stated in a Fox News March 26 interview that he had been accused of being xenophobic and a racist for stopping travelers from China coming into the country.

On February 11, the virus officially received a new name: COVID-19.

Twenty-five countries had confirmed cases by February 13.

February 14 saw the first death in Europe, identified as a Chinese tourist in France. The first case was also reported in Egypt, therefore indicative of the involvement of another continent.

Between February 12-21, outbreaks soared in South Korea, Iran, and Italy, and the first death on American soil, in the state of Washington, was recorded on February 29. He was a man in his 50s, reportedly with underlying health conditions, yet with no known evidence of having contracted the illness through travel. At the same time, health officials in Washington reported that 27 patients and 25 staff members at the Life Care Center in Kirkland, Washington State, displayed symptoms associated with Covid-19. President Trump said that the death seemed to have happened, "overnight."

The Dow Jones closed at 29,219.98 on February 20, 2020.

The FTSE closed at 5,935.98 on February 20, 2020.

By this time, South Korea announced more than 800 new cases, bringing their confirmed cases to 3,150, and the world was introduced to the concept of Social Distancing, as South Korea's Vice Health Minister, Kim Kang-lip asked his people to, "Please stay at home and refrain from going outside and minimize contact with other people." At this stage, South Korea had the second largest number of cases outside of China, with Iran, Lebanon, Israel, and Egypt reporting an increase in their number of cases.

On February 24, the President's office sent a budget request to Congress for $2.5 billion to fight the impact of the virus. Sent from the Executive Office of the President and signed by Russell T. Vought, Acting Director, he explained that:

At the direction of the President and under the auspices of the Task Force, several Federal agencies are contributing significant resources and personnel to support the domestic and international response. To this point, no agency has been inhibited in response efforts due to resources or authorities. However, much is still unknown about this virus and the disease it causes. The Administration believes additional Federal resources are necessary to take steps to prepare for a potential worsening of the situation in the United States, and requests an appropriation of $1.25 billion of emergency funding in the Public Health and Social Services Emergency Fund at HHS to continue supporting critical response and preparedness activities. In addition, the Administration is requesting that the Congress permit the $535 million in emergency supplemental funding appropriated in the Agriculture, Rural Development, Food and Drug Administration, and Related Agencies Appropriations Act, 2020, to the Public Health and Social Services Emergency Fund at HHS for the prevention and treatment of Ebola to be used for COVID-19 response. Tremendous progress has been made on Ebola and the current national response priority should be COVID-19. These two proposals would make $1.8 billion in new resources available for the current response.

It continued:

This funding would support all aspects of the US response, including: public health preparedness and response efforts; public health surveillance, epidemiology, laboratory testing, and quarantining costs; advanced research and development of new vaccines, therapeutics, and diagnostics; advanced manufacturing enhancements; and the Strategic National Stockpile. Funds would also be made available, as necessary, to affected States that are making contributions to the current national response.

Switzerland, Austria, Croatia and Algeria declared their first cases on February 25.

Also on February 25, the NIH announced the commencement of a clinical trial to evaluate the antiviral Gilead Sciences Inc. drug named Remdesivir at the University of Nebraska Medical Center in Omaha, Nebraska. The trial's first participant had been repatriated from the Diamond Princess. NIAID Director and US Coronavirus Task Force member, Dr. Anthony Fauci, clarified that, "We urgently need a safe and effective treatment for COVID-19. Although Remdesivir has been administered to some patients with COVID-19, we do not have solid data to indicate it can improve clinical outcomes," adding that, "A randomized, placebo-controlled trial is the gold standard for determining if an experimental treatment can benefit patients." This trial, led by Andre Kalil, M.D., a professor of internal medicine at UNMC, was assigned to lead the trial, where 13 repatriated participants from the Diamond Princess were allegedly transported to the National Quarantine Unit in Omaha on February 17, 2020.

As the clinical trials commenced, several towns and villages in the Lombardy Region of Italy were placed in a lockdown. The next day, February 26, marked the first assumed "community spread" US death, in California. The patient had no known travel history or contact with another patient. This day also witnessed President Trump assigning Vice President Mike Pence to spearhead the US government response to the virus containment efforts.

While community spread was being confirmed in California, the countries of Brazil, Greece, Georgia, North Macedonia, Romania, Pakistan, and Norway declared their first cases. San Marino, The Netherlands, Nigeria, Denmark and Estonia joined the list within 24 hours. By February 28, a total of 56 countries suffered from Coronavirus as Belarus, New Zealand, Iceland, Mexico, Monaco, and Azerbaijan announced their first cases.

The Dow Jones closed at 25,766.64 on February 28, 2020.
The FTSE closed at 6,580.61 on February 28, 2020.

By March 3, Iran announced that 23 of their Parliament had tested positive for COVID-19.

As the countries of Andorra, Indonesia, Morocco, Saudi Arabia, Tunisia, Senegal, Jordan, Portugal, Armenia, the Czech Republic, and the Ukraine confirmed first cases, the number of cases in England had risen to 23, and France reported 73 on March 6. Later that day, Dr. Peter Hotez, Dean at the School of Tropical Medicine at Baylor College of Medicine, addressed Congress, referring to the new virus sweeping across America as, "The angel of death for older people."

Countries across the globe were announcing their first case, just as states across America were also announcing their first cases as the virus swiftly sped across the country. As previously mentioned, the first state to be impacted was Washington State on January 20. The infection then traveled across our northern border to Canada, who reported their first case on January 25. The city of Chicago in Illinois saw the second US case on January 24, also in an individual who had traveled from Wuhan, with America's third case arising in Orange County, California, once again in a traveler from the Wuhan area of China. America's fourth and fifth cases were identified on January 26 in California and Arizona. All had recently traveled to Wuhan in China. The sixth case in the US marked the first case in an individual who had not traveled to Wuhan, but who lived with an individual who had recently been to the infected area of China, was announced on January 30, with the last day in January marking the seventh case in another patient in California, and also in another who had recently traveled to Wuhan. The eighth case was declared in Boston the next day in a university student, also who had recently returned from Wuhan. There were 11 cases by February 2: one in Washington state, two in Illinois, six in California, one in Massachusetts, and one in Arizona. More states were soon to have their first cases of this frightening contagion.

Until this time, the CDC had recommended restrictions that limited testing to only those in the general public who had close contact with someone who was confirmed with the virus. The alteration was made at this time to allow physicians to use their judgment based on signs and symptoms.

New York reported its first case on March 1, and New Jersey reported its first case on March 5, with Kentucky and Oklahoma reporting their first cases the next day, and Kansas reporting positive cases within the next 24 hours along with DC. Several states were beginning to declare a State of Emergency as the spread continued at an alarming pace. It resembled trying to put out a fire in a haystack as the first cases were reported, and first deaths declared, state after state, city after city, home after home.

The Dow Jones closed at 25,864.78 on March 6, 2020.

The FTSE closed at 6,462.55 on March 6, 2020.

March 6 also saw President Trump signing an 8.3 billion Coronavirus Response Bill in answer to his request made 10 days earlier. As he signed the document, the President told reporters that, "I asked for two and a half, and I got 8.3."

The bill was reportedly introduced by Rep. Nita Lowey, the Democratic Chairman of the House Committee on Appropriations, with the intent to provide assistance created by COVID. The $8.3 billion bill included:

- An excess of $3 billion for research and development of vaccines and more than $800 million for research regarding treatments.
- An excess of $2 billion was apportioned for the Centers for Disease Control and Prevention, with $61 million to the US Food and Drug Administration.
- The US Agency for International Development was to receive more than $1 billion.
- An excess of $1 billion would go to the state and local public heath efforts.
- It also authorized roughly $500 million to allow for Medicare providers to administer telehealth services.

On March 8, the Italian Prime Minister, Guiseppe Conte, expanded his travel restrictions to the entire Lombardy Region, also adding 14 additional provinces and additionally increasing restrictions on movements to over 10 million citizens, increasing this again the following day to place the entire country in a lockdown.

The escalating numbers of deaths and infected seemed to accelerate with the same fervor that economies continued to plummet, and on March 9 the stock market circuit breakers were triggered for the first time on 20 years as fears escalated about not only virus deaths, but also questions about economic disaster. People saw their hard-earned savings and pensions collapsing, with some disappearing, with mounting tensions, and a new price war between the Russians and the Saudis as energy stocks such as Exxon Mobil buckled 12 percent, representing its lowest close since 2004. The Stock Market circuit breakers kicked in at 9:33 AM, a mere three minutes after the market opened when the S&P 500 dropped by 7 percent. This triggered a 15-minute halt of all stocks with the intention of pausing the market to create liquidity. Stocks rallied slightly after the markets opened again at 10:49 AM, closing on March 9 at 23,851.02, only to see the circuit breaker triggered again the next day, once again only minutes after the opening bell. At the time of writing this account, March 9 is identified as the commencement of the 2020 stock market crash, which was followed by two more record-setting point drops on March 12, where the DOW closed at 21,200.62, representing a 9.99 percent drop, and again on March 16, where it plunged 12.93 percent, breaking the record of the 1929 Black Monday freefall of 12.82 percent.

On March 10, Vice President Mike Pence announced that there would be no co-pays for coronavirus treatment. President Trump restricted travel the next day, March 11, from Europe to America with the hope of curtailing the spread of the contagion. It was a "temporary" suspension that would commence on Friday, March 13, set to last for 30 days, yet stipulating that this action would not apply to U.S. citizens or to travelers from the UK. He elaborated on the various restrictions in his speech, which was backed up by a publicized White House announcement to clarify all restrictions that would apply. It also clarified the process, and dictated to the airports:

Effective for flights taking off at 11:59 PM EDT on Friday, March 13, Americans returning from all restricted countries will now be required to travel through the following 13 airports:

- *Boston-Logan International Airport (BOS), Massachusetts*
- *Chicago O'Hare International Airport (ORD), Illinois*
- *Dallas/Fort Worth International Airport (DFW), Texas*
- *Detroit Metropolitan Airport (DTW), Michigan*
- *Daniel K. Inouye International Airport (HNL), Hawaii*
- *Hartsfield-Jackson Atlanta International Airport (ATL), Georgia*
- *John F. Kennedy International Airport (JFK), New York*
- *Los Angeles International Airport, (LAX), California*
- *Miami International Airport (MIA), Florida*
- *Newark Liberty International Airport (EWR), New Jersey*
- *San Francisco International Airport (SFO), California*
- *Seattle-Tacoma International Airport (SEA), Washington*
- *Washington-Dulles International Airport (IAD), Virginia*

Upon arrival, travelers will proceed to standard customs processing. They will then continue to enhanced entry screening where the passenger will be asked about their medical history, current condition, and asked for contact information for local health authorities. Passengers will then be given written guidance about COVID-19 and directed to proceed to their final destination, and immediately home-quarantine in accordance with CDC best practices.

I was delighted to see that we were closing the back door, but we were soon to learn that some of the windows still remained open.

North Dakota had reported its first case of the virus on March 11, with Kansas reporting their first case within 24-hours afterwards. The WHO, also on March 11, officially declared the outbreak as a PANDEMIC. March 11 also saw the Dow Jones Industrial Average ending an eleven-year bull market run and entering a bear market.

The Dow Jones closed at 21,200.62 on March 12, 2020.
The FTSE closed at 5,904.05 on March 12, 2020.

I had spent decades traveling frequently, and through my travels I had acquired a very dear friend, Joan, who still travels with the same alacrity that we used to share. As for me, my suitcases are mostly in retirement. I was unsure if Joan was in the country or in some remote area of the world, so I reached out to her. After several unanswered calls, I sent an e-mail on the afternoon of Friday,

March 13, the day when the new restrictions would commence at midnight:

Hi Joan,

I have tried calling you, and just wanted to make sure that you are okay – probably on a nice island somewhere without all this virus. Anyway, hope you are well.

– Cheri

Her response:

Sent: Fri, Mar 13, 2020 9:39 pm

Hi Cheri,

I saw you called a few times, however I have been traveling and needed to wait until I return to Margaret River before I can return your call.

A friend and I have been traveling together for the last two plus weeks. He is on an around-the-world trip. We met up in Hobart for a few days, onto Melbourne with a week's stay in Margaret River before going to Kathmandu.

We arrived during Holi, a festival where people throw colored powder at each other. The following day we took a helicopter to base camp. Seeing the Himalayas was amazing. We visited a few temples before heading off to Pokhara from which you get a great view of Annapurna.

Now on my way back to WA.

Better get going for my next flight.

XOXOX,

Joan

Did she not know about the virus? Her trips usually lasted weeks. WA? Was she headed back to the US through Washington State, or was this a typo, or had she meant MA for Massachusetts, where I was? She is a native New Yorker and lives mostly in Manhattan. I needed to warn her.

Fired off immediately:

Dear Joan,

Nice to hear good news these days. I loved Kathmandu and the Himalayas. And you met someone! Outstanding, and I am so happy for you...

You mentioned coming back to WA – Washington State? Or did you mean MA? Have a safe flight.

PANDEMIC 2020

Joan, do be careful! The USA you knew 2 weeks ago is very different now with this virus, and WA is the hardest hit, CA next, Illinois, then NY. MA is about fifth. All but 2 states have it. MA, and most of the county schools are closing; you cannot buy hand sanitizer anywhere...or toilet paper (go figure). Just about every state has declared a state of emergency and the country is beginning to lock down. Italy has already locked down tight, basically house arrest, only one person in a family allowed out to buy groceries, maintaining a 1-meter distance.

The stock market is now a bear market (it went up yesterday after the FED dumped "trillions" into it - second time in a week, but I suspect it will crash again on Monday. People are panicked and overreacting - although there are currently 146,000 cases of this virus in the world, 80,000+ in China, 5,445 deaths. News on-line shows that "China has responded to the spread of coronavirus to Tibet by cracking down on people who post information about the deadly virus..." You may not be up to date.

The WHO has declared this a pandemic. International flights are banned to the USA except from the UK. Cruise ships are blocked. The situation is changing daily. Aside from wanting to say "hi", that is why I was checking on you to see that you are safe. Margaret River is probably fine. The cape has no cases as yet. The UK has less cases, but also less people than the USA, and their increase is rising faster than ours. Stay safe my friend. Call me please when you are back.

Lots of love,
Cheri

I worried about my friend. Travel had been suspended, yet flights were still going, and coming, and the media showed massive crowds at the airports as everyone scrambled to return home. I would need to wait for her reply.

A US National State of Emergency was declared on March 13.

President Trump sent a letter on March 13 to Secretary Wolf, Secretary Mnuchin, Secretary Azar, and Administrator Gaynor regarding his determination under the Stafford Act. It stated that, "I have determined that the ongoing Coronavirus Disease 2019 (COVID-19) pandemic is of sufficient severity and magnitude to warrant an emergency determination under section 501(b) of the Robert T. Stafford Disaster Relief and Emergency Assistance Act, 42 U.S.C. 5121-5207 (the "Stafford Act")." Trump clarified that:

Cheryl Powell

My decision to make this determination pursuant to section 501(b) of the Stafford Act is based on the fact that our entire country is now facing a significant public health emergency. The World Health Organization has officially declared that we are in the midst of a global pandemic. As of the date of this declaration, 32 states, 3 territories, 4 tribes, and 1 tribal nation, spread geographically across our country, have declared a state of emergency as a result of the virus. Only the Federal Government can provide the necessary coordination to address a pandemic of this national size and scope caused by a pathogen introduced into our country. It is the preeminent responsibility of the Federal Government to take action to stem a nationwide pandemic that has its origins abroad, which implicates its authority to regulate matters related to interstate matters and foreign commerce and to conduct the foreign relations of the United States...This pandemic has the potential to cause severe consequences for our country's national and economic security. Based on the advice of public health officials, I have already taken stringent measures to restrict travel to the United States of foreign nationals who have been recently physically present in certain countries that pose a threat of intensifying the spread of COVID-19 within our country. And HHS and CDC have taken effective action to address the public health threat posed by COVID-19. While these actions have been in the best interest of the health of our people, COVID-19 has the potential to impose a temporary financial hardship on all Americans. It is therefore critical that we deploy all powers and authorities available to the Federal Government to provide needed relief...as an initial step, I hereby determine, under section 501(b) of the Stafford Act, that an emergency exists nationwide.

He concluded with:

In accordance with this determination, the Federal Emergency Management Agency may provide, as appropriate, assistance pursuant to section 502 and 503 of the Stafford Act for emergency protective measures not authorized under other Federal statutes. Administrator Gaynor shall coordinate and direct other Federal agencies in providing needed assistance under the Stafford Act, subject to the Department of Health and Human Services' role as the lead Federal agency for the Federal Government's response to COVID-19...I have encouraged all State and local governments to activate their Emergency Operations Centers and to review their emergency preparedness plans...I am also instructing Secretary Mnuchin to provide relief from tax deadlines to Americans who have been adversely affected by the COVID-19 emergency, as appropriate, pursuant to 26 U.S.C. 7508A(a)...I encourage all governors and tribal leaders to consider requesting Federal assistance under this provision of the Stafford Act, pursuant to the statutory criteria. I stand ready to expeditiously consider any such request.

Also on March 13, the House reached an agreement to pass the Families First Coronavirus Response Act (FFCRA). This required certain employers to provide their employees with paid sick leave or expanded family and medical leave. The Department of Labor's Wage and Hour Division (WHD) would administer and enforce the new law's paid leave requirements according to specified reasons, with the provisions within the act applying, initially, through December 31, 2020.

The number of countries infected with the virus rose to 121 on March 13. On this day, the NBA cancelled its season.

Of note on March 15 was a transcript of a press conference call held with the 16th Chairman of the Federal Reserve, Jerome Powell, having served in that office since February of 2018 after being nominated for the position by President Donald Trump and receiving confirmation by the US Senate. His transcript stated that:

Today the Federal Reserve took a number of actions to support American families and business and the economy overall and to promote the flow of credit as we weather disruptions caused by the coronavirus. The virus is having a profound effect on people across the United States and around the world. On behalf of my colleagues at the Federal Reserve, our first concern is for those who've been harmed...

Continuing later with:

The Federal Reserve's role is guided by our mandate from Congress to promote maximum employment and stable prices for the American people, along with our responsibilities to promote the stability of the financial system. Today we reduced the target range for our policy interest rate by one percentage point, bringing it close to zero, and said that we expect to maintain the rate at this level until we're confident that the economy has weathered recent events and is on track to achieve our maximum employment and price stability goals. In addition, we took other actions to support the flow of credit to households and businesses.

Further in the transcript, he expounds with:

I won't go into detail on the other actions we took today, but they involved eliminating reserve requirements for banks and encouraging banks to make use of intraday credit with the Federal Reserve and to use their capital and liquidity buffers as they support lending to households and businesses.

But was it enough?

March 15: (WORLD)

Total world cases: 169,524

Deaths: 6,515

Recovered: 77,753

Active Cases: 85,256, Mild:79,335 (93%), Critical: 5,921 (7%),

Closed: 84,268

I received a reply from Joan on March 15:

Dear Cheri,

Sorry for the confusion, WA is Western Australia.

Nepal felt very safe with no outbreak yet, but the poor Nepalese depend on tourism, so they will be very badly impacted. I must say, I did enjoy my stay...

Thank you for all of your good advice. I am just hoping that I will not be locked down in Australia. I am scheduled to leave next Monday, but just saw a message about self-quarantining if you have traveled outside of Australia. Ugh!

I will call when I return.

XOXOXO,
Joan

March 16: (WORLD- early morning figures)

Total world cases: 170,438

Deaths: 6,526

Recovered: 77,790

Mild: 80,195 (93 %)

Critical: 5,927 (7%)

As a mental health practitioner, my interactions seemed to change almost overnight, and every day thereafter as I and everyone else entered this runaway roller coaster. My career is devoted to helping those with a myriad of difficulties, but COVID-19 suddenly became the chief topic with some of my patients, friends, and neighbors all beginning to sound the same, asking if this was Armageddon and likening COVID-19 to the Black Plague and the End of the World. One of my best friends asked if suicide was a plausible solution. Definitely not! What I still tried to instill in patients, neighbors, and friends is hope, and perspective. It seemed as if the world had gone mad. The media reflected little difference, covering the pandemic 24/7, with other channels frequently offering little relief where one might watch law enforcement shows and criminal investigations, more death and courtroom dramas.

The virus was discussed at our staff meeting on Wednesday, March 11. We discussed not only the uneasiness of our patients, but also our own apprehensions, trying to problem solve possibilities and probabilities in a highly charged and rapidly changing emergency situation. Our director brought us up to date, and I remember, fondly, her remark to add levity to the atmosphere, "What I want to know is what happened to all the toilet paper."

Although it was initially believed that children and the young were relatively immune to the virus, there was a question as to whether or not their exposure to other children while at school was such that they were the bringing the virus home to unwittingly infect the older population. Amidst a frenzy of State of Emergency declarations, schools began to be impacted, and March 12 saw the beginning of 2-week school closures as Ohio announced that it would be closing all schools at least until April 3, with France, Portugal, Norway and Israel closing all schools. By March 15, 29 states had announced school closures.

On March 16, the White House's evening newsletter announced that:

This afternoon, President Trump and the White House Coronavirus Task Force issued new guidelines to help protect Americans during the global Coronavirus outbreak." It asked every American to help to slow the spread to protect the American people and to protect high-risk populations. It recommended listening to state and local authorities, staying home if you feel sick, keeping children home if sick, keeping the entire household home if a family member tested positive, remaining home if you have underlying health conditions or are elderly, and washing hands for 20-seconds and wiping down surfaces regularly.

March 16: (WORLD – late evening figures)
Total world cases: 181,344
Deaths: 7,130
Recovered: 78,339
Mild: 90,054 (94%)

> **The Dow Jones closed at 20,188.52 on March 16, 2020.**
> **The FTSE closed at 5,935.98 on March 16, 2020.**

Uzbekistan, Kazakhstan, Somalia, Turkey, and Guatemala added their countries to the growing list of those with virus cases by March 17.

Some of the clinicians began working from home after the governor of Massachusetts, Charlie Baker, made an announcement that officials had met with insurance companies and that Telehealth was approved. I therefore commenced working from home the next day, a Thursday, only to be called back into the office the following week, where we were instructed to perform our telephone sessions from the office. The following day, March 17, the US Department of Health and Human Services released an "immediate" announcement that, "OCR (Office of Civil Rights) Announces Notification of Enforcement Discretion for Telehealth Remote Communications During the COVID-19 Nationwide Public Health Emergency." The announcement also waived potential penalties for HIPPA violations against health care workers using everyday communication technologies, provided these were used in "good faith." We again began working from home in what was initially announced would be a 2-week stay-at-home order that spread swiftly across the country.

Alas, the media had new headlines and viewers increased almost as rapidly as the number of those infected increased, accompanied by a simultaneous nose-dive in the US and world economies.

A 100-page federal plan was released on March 17 that revealed a plan to combat the virus, warning that the pandemic might well "last 18 months or longer" and come in "multiple waves."

So, I was at home, calling patients daily, occasionally on weekends. The goal was to maintain safety, especially for some of my more medically compromised patients such as the elderly, and/or for those with other medical issues such as severe obesity, diabetes, cancer, kidney disease, cardiac problems, or similar conditions due to their being singled out in advisories as being more vulnerable to the virus. The youngest patient I have had in my caseload was aged two, with the oldest being aged 98, treating all diagnoses included in the Diagnostic and Statistical Manual (DSM), and even this new disease, where it my intention to request that the Board consider identifying in the next revision of mental health disorders, which I am currently treating, yet cannot officially diagnose, as Crisis Anxiety.

The reactions I was dealing with in patients and non-patients did not fully fit into any specific current diagnosis, yet presented more as a combination of Post Traumatic Stress Disorder (PTSD), depression, Acute Stress Disorder, Anxiety Disorder, Panic Attacks, and just plain fear.

Post Traumatic Stress Disorder (PTSD) is a psychological disorder that can occur in people who have experienced or witnessed a traumatic event. I say "can" because not all who have witnessed or experienced a traumatic event respond with PTSD symptomatology, and not all traumatic events are the same and can include terrorist acts, combat, rape or other personal assaults from beating, or other such violent attacks, and even natural disasters – inclusive of floods, hurricanes, tornadoes, and even epidemics and pandemics.

It was once believed that such symptoms only pertained to soldiers, hence the previous terms of "combat fatigue" and "shell shock", but PTSD can arise in anyone, of any age, and any race. According to the Anxiety and Depression Association of America (ADAA):

More than 8 million Americans between the age of 18 and older have PTSD. 3.6% of the US Adult population experienced post-traumatic stress disorder (PTSD) in the past year, 67 percent of people exposed to mass violence have been shown to develop PTSD, a higher rate than those exposed to natural disasters or other types of traumatic events. People who have experienced previous traumatic events run a higher risk of developing PTSD. PTSD can also affect children, and members of the military.

According to the DSM, there are eight criteria for a PTSD diagnosis:

The following criteria apply to adults, adolescents, and children older than 6 years. For children 6 years and younger, see the DSM-5 section titled "Post Traumatic Stress Disorder for Children 6 Years and Younger"(APA, 2013a).

A   Exposure to actual or threatened death, serious injury, or sexual violence in one (or more) of the following ways:

    1.   Directly experiencing the traumatic event(s).

    2.   Witnessing, in person, the event(s) as it occurred to others.

    3.   Learning that the traumatic event(s) occurred to a close family member or close friend. In cases of actual or threatened death of a family member or friend, the event(s) must have been violent or accidental.

    4.   Experiencing repeated or extreme exposure to aversive details of the traumatic event(s) (e.g., first responders collecting human remains; police officers repeatedly exposed to details of child abuse). Note: Criterion A4 does not apply to exposure through electronic media, television, movies, or pictures, unless this exposure is work related.

B. Presence of one (or more) of the following intrusion symptoms associated with the traumatic event(s), beginning after the traumatic event(s) occurred:

    1.   Recurrent, involuntary, and intrusive distressing memories of the traumatic event(s). Note: In children older than 6 years, repetitive play may occur in which themes or aspects of the traumatic event(s) are expressed.

    2.   Recurrent distressing dreams in which the content and/or affect of the dream are related to the traumatic event(s). Note: In children, there may be frightening dreams without recognizable content.

    3.   Dissociative reactions (e.g., flashbacks) in which the individual feels or acts as if the traumatic event(s) were recurring. (Such reactions may occur on a continuum, with the most extreme expression being a complete loss of awareness of present surroundings.) Note: In children, trauma-specific reenactment may occur in play.

    4.   Intense or prolonged psychological distress at exposure to internal or external cues that symbolize or resemble an aspect of the traumatic event(s).

5. Marked physiological reactions to internal or external cues that symbolize or resemble an aspect of the traumatic event(s).

C. Persistent avoidance of stimuli associated with the traumatic event(s), beginning after the traumatic event(s) occurred, as evidenced by one or both of the following:

1. Avoidance of or efforts to avoid distressing memories, thoughts, or feelings about or closely associated with the traumatic event(s).

2. Avoidance of or efforts to avoid external reminders (people, places, conversations, activities, objects, situations) that arouse distressing memories, thoughts, or feelings about or closely associated with the traumatic event(s).

D. Negative alterations in cognitions and mood associated with the traumatic event(s), beginning or worsening after the traumatic event(s) occurred, as evidenced by two (or more) of the following:

1. Inability to remember an important aspect of the traumatic event(s) (typically due to dissociative amnesia, and not to other factors such as head injury, alcohol, or drugs).

2. Persistent and exaggerated negative beliefs or expectations about oneself, others, or the world (e.g., "I am bad," "No one can be trusted," "The world is completely dangerous," "My whole nervous system is permanently ruined").

3. Persistent, distorted cognitions about the cause or consequences of the traumatic event(s) that lead the individual to blame himself/herself or others.

4. Persistent negative emotional state (e.g., fear, horror, anger, guilt, or shame).

5. Markedly diminished interest or participation in significant activities.

6. Feelings of detachment or estrangement from others.

7. Persistent inability to experience positive emotions (e.g., inability to experience happiness, satisfaction, or loving feelings).

E. Marked alterations in arousal and reactivity associated with the traumatic event(s), beginning or worsening after the traumatic event(s) occurred, as evidenced by two (or more) of the following:
1. Irritable behavior and angry outbursts (with little or no provocation), typically expressed as verbal or physical aggression toward people or objects.
2. Reckless or self-destructive behavior.
3. Hypervigilance.
4. Exaggerated startle response.
5. Problems with concentration.
6. Sleep disturbance (e.g., difficulty falling or staying asleep or restless sleep).

F. Duration of the disturbance (Criteria B, C, D and E) is more than 1 month.

G. The disturbance causes clinically significant distress or impairment in social, occupational, or other important areas of functioning.

H. The disturbance is not attributable to the physiological effects of a substance (e.g., medication, alcohol) or another medical condition.

Specify whether:

With dissociative symptoms: The individual's symptoms meet the criteria for Post Traumatic Stress Disorder, and in addition, in response to the stressor, the individual experiences persistent or recurrent symptoms of either of the following:
1 Depersonalization: Persistent or recurrent experiences of feeling detached from, and as if one were an outside observer of, one's mental processes or body (e.g., feeling as though one were in a dream; feeling a sense of unreality of self or body or of time moving slowly).
2. Derealization: Persistent or recurrent experiences of unreality of surroundings (e.g., the world around the individual is experienced as unreal, dreamlike, distant, or distorted). Note: To use this subtype, the dissociative symptoms must not be attributable to the physiological effects of a substance (e.g., blackouts, behavior during alcohol intoxication) or another medical condition (e.g., complex partial seizures).

Specify whether:

With delayed expression: If the full diagnostic criteria are not met until at least 6 months after the event (although the onset and expression of some symptoms may be immediate).

Source: APA, 2013, pp. 271-272

According to the DSM, (pg 276), "In the United States, projected lifetime risk for PTSD using DSM-IV criteria at age 75 years is 8.7%. Twelve month prevalence among US adults is about 3.5%." The DSM goes on (pg. 277) to clarify that, "Duration of the symptoms also varies, with complete recovery within 3 months occurring in approximately one-half of adults, while some individuals remain symptomatic for longer than twelve months and sometimes more than 50 years."

It seemed like almost overnight I was adding treatment of PTSD or symptoms of a similar diagnosis to my patient's care plans, and seeing similar symptoms in friends, neighbors, and even myself. Of course, not everyone who is exposed to events acquire PTSD. Some have formed enough resilience through life with better coping skills and resilience. Others hide or mask their symptoms and reactions, or their symptoms take another direction, such as Acute Stress Disorder, where the symptoms again occur in response to a traumatic event. However, with Acute Stress Disorder the duration of the symptoms is three days to one month after the event. As with PTSD, these individuals may relive the trauma, have flashbacks and/or nightmares. They may feel numb or detached from themselves, and the overall symptoms can cause major distress and often difficulties in their daily lives. If the symptoms are resolved within three days, then the individual does not meet the criteria for this disorder. Nevertheless, it is generally believed that roughly half of those with Acute Stress Disorder go on to have PTSD. According to the DSM (pg. 284), "Acute Stress Disorder tends to be identified in less than 20% of cases following traumatic events that do not involve interpersonal assault," going on to later clarify that, "Higher rates (i.e. 20%-50%) are reported following interpersonal traumatic events, including assault, rape, and witnessing a mass shooting."

Next on the list of increased diagnoses were the Adjustment Disorders, usually arising when having difficulties coping with a single or variety of stressful life events that include major life changes, moving to a new house, state or country, financial difficulties, illness and health concerns, divorce or relationship difficulties, dealing with the passing of someone close, and sudden disasters.

Once again, while everyone has stress in their lives, some are more prone to feeling overwhelmed, while others enjoy having a wider basket of emotional tools to help them through such events, while an inability to adjust to stressful events can create one or more psychological, and sometimes physical, symptoms in this disorder that generally does not last more than six months, unless the stressor remains.

Several of the symptoms that arise with adjustment disorders include, but are not limited to: crying, a lack of concentration, feeling withdrawn, trapped, or helpless, being anxious, possibly impulsive actions/reactions, fatigue, indigestion, insomnia, and suicidal ideation.

The six different types of adjustment disorders are: Adjustment Disorder with Depressed Mood, Adjustment Disorder with Anxiety, Adjustment Disorder with Mixed Anxiety and Depressed Mood, Adjustment Disorder with Disturbance of Conduct, Adjustment Disorder with Mixed Disturbance of Emotions and Conduct, and Adjustment Disorder Unspecified – the latter being where the symptoms do not fit better into one of the other categories and often pertain to difficulties arising with family, friends, or in a school or work environment.

I saw a myriad increase in all of these, and more such as general anxiety, depression, and conduct disorders with children. Even worse, their therapist now shared some of their symptoms. The abnormal was becoming the new normal.

March 17: (WORLD)
Total world cases: 186,665
Deaths: 7,467
Recovered: 80,889 (91%)
Active Cases: 102,506, Mild: 95,985, Critical: 6,521 (6%)

March 17: (USA)
Total cases: 5,696
New Cases: 1,033
Deaths: 97

Recovered: 74
Active Cases: 5,525
> The Dow Jones closed at 21,237.38 on March 17, 2020.
> The FTSE closed at 5,294.90 on March 17, 2020.

March 18: (WORLD)
Total world cases: 194,750
Deaths: 7,896
Recovered: 81,080
Active Cases: 105,774, Mild: 99,044 (94%), Critical: 6,730 (6 %),
Closed: 88,976

March 18: (USA)
Total cases: 6,524
New Cases: 113
Deaths: 116
New Deaths: 7
Recovered: 106
Active Cases: 6,302

The Dow Jones closed at 19,898.92 on March 18, 2020. This was the first time it had been this low since February of 2017, with the Dow being 6.3% down, or 1,338 points on the day, erasing nearly all the gains made since President Trump had taken office.

Also on March 18, President Trump signed a second COVID aid package to provide a new round of emergency funding. The new legislation allowed for paid sick and family leave for some of the US workers impacted by the illness. It also expanded unemployment assistance and increased testing resources.

March 19: (WORLD)
Total world cases: 219,020
Deaths: 8,953 (10%)
Recovered: 84,795 (90%)
Active Cases: 125,264, Mild: 118,106, Critical: 7,158

March 19: (USA) – morning
Total cases: 9,464
Deaths: 205
Recovered: 108
Active Cases: 9,201, Mild: 79,335, Critical: 64

March 19: (USA) – evening
Total cases: 14,315
New Cases: 526
Deaths: 218
Recovered: 121
Active cases: 13,976, Mild: 79,335, Critical: 64
The Dow Jones closed at 19.173.98 on March 19, 2020.
The FTSE closed at 5,151.61 on March 19, 2020.

The Bank of England cut its interest rates to 0.1% in the hope of stabilizing markets.

On March 20, Italy announced that their country had suffered 627 deaths, which represented the largest single increase since the outbreak of the pandemic. On the same day, the WHO delivered an excess of 1.5 million test kits around the world. Also on this day, Egypt closed all mosques and churches at the same time that China reported its third consecutive day of having no new cases. In America, President Trump signed the Families First Coronavirus Response Act into law.

In a long overdue glimmer of positive events, China declared that they had no new locally spread infections for the first time on March 19. Three days later, New York City reported 21,000 cases.

On the other side of the world, the USS Theodore Roosevelt, announced its first sailor to test positive for the virus. It was reported that the ship had made a port call on March 5 at Da Nang in Vietnam, where several of the crew had stayed at a hotel where two people had tested positive. What was happening on land was now also expanding at sea.

Back in the United States, the Dow Jones closed at 18,591.93 on March 23 as politicians struggled to reach an agreement on a fiscal stimulus package that could further address the economic freefall due to the pandemic. It was 582.05 points lower, which was the lowest level since November of 2016. US Treasury Secretary Steven Mnuchin was quoted from an interview with CNBC's Jim Cramer as stating that, "We're using some of the funds we have, but we need Congress to approve additional funds today so that we can move forward and support American workers and the American economy."

The failure of the markets on March 23, according to a CNN business article by Anneken Tappe, was due to the, "Senate Democrats blocked a coronavirus economic stimulus bill from advancing. It was the second time in two days Democrats blocked the measure as talks over the giant bill continue."

The FTSE closed at 4,993.89 on March 23, 2020.

Shinzo Abe, Japan's Prime Minister, announced on March 24 that he and the International Olympic Committee President, Thomas Bach, had agreed to postpone the summer Olympics until 2021. It is worth noting that the Olympics have been cancelled three times since the first Olympics were first held in 1896. The three cancellations were all due to war, World War I in 1916, and World War II in 1940 and 1944. Until 2020, the Olympics had never postponed.

Back in the United States, the Dow Jones Industrial Average soared in response to news that lawmakers were very close to an agreement on a giant stimulus package to ease the economic fallout, representing the largest single day gain since 1933. By this time, records were being reset almost daily, and not only pertaining to economic jumps and plunges. On March 24, Italy had 63,927 cases and 6,077 deaths. Spain had 33,089 cases and 2,182 deaths. The United Kingdom had 6,650 cases and 335 deaths.

The Dow seemed to leap in gratitude to the government aid on March 24 in response to news that agreements were being reached regarding the new stimulus bill, with markets soaring 2,112 points in the final hour of trading, shattering a single day record that had only recently been set just over a week beforehand, inauspiciously set on Friday the thirteenth. The index gained nearly

11.4 percent on March 24, with the S&P gaining 9.3 and the Nasdaq over 8.1 percent, representing the most since 1933. Shattering records was also becoming part of the new normal.

Also on Tuesday, March 24, President Trump announced during a Fox News interview that ultimately the goal is to reopen the country, suggesting that, April 12 would be "a beautiful time" (Easter) "to reopen the country." He explained that, "I would love to have the country opened up and raring to go by Easter," adding that, "I hope we can do this by Easter...we're all working very hard to make that a reality." He continued to clarify that the, "First priority is always the health and safety of the American people and we're continuing to evaluate the data."

He was criticized harshly for suggesting such an early date. I liked his idea, but I admit that it seemed somewhat unrealistic. Never before, until this month of March in 2020, had I ever written to the President, mostly I suppose because I suspected that communications were greatly filtered or simply discarded – yet I took a chance and sent a suggestion that he indeed open the country for Easter – through a widely televised service of hope, remembrance and prayer for all faiths. This would include a Catholic portion, Christian, Jewish, and Muslim portions.

I agreed with the need to get our nation back on track, but I suspected that time would be nearer to mid-May, that it would be patchy at first, and that we would all be living in a new, changed, reality that would forever include new daily terms such as "social distancing" and "herding" and "hoarding" – but I thought it should also include words such as "resilience" and "hope" and "healing." We needed to be careful not to lose our "humanity" – the best of who we are, and who we can become through this. I proposed that he unify the country in an Easter celebration of hope, remembrance, prayer and healing, to include ALL faiths and ALL races, indeed ALL countries. Easter may not be a part of all religions, but the concepts of healing, compassion, and resurrection apply to all of humanity.

By March 25, the world number of deaths had increased to 21,185, with 468,577 cases. Of those infected worldwide, 65,797 cases were located in America, with 935 deaths. The USS Roosevelt now had 9 cases, with "dozens" reported soon afterwards.

44

Also on March 25, following several days of partisan squabbling and haggling reminiscent of the all-to-recent failed impeachment episode, an agreement was finally reached, marking the most expensive economic emergency package in US history, resulting in a roughly $2 trillion rescue package to address the dwindling economy due to the virus. It included the following:

- One-time direct payments of up to $1,200 for individuals and $2,400 for couples, with $500 added for every child. This would be based on the 2019 tax returns for those who filed them and the tax 2018 information if they had not yet filed their 2019 return. The benefit would phase out above $75,000 in income for individuals and $150,000 for couples, disappearing completely at the $99,000 and $198,000 thresholds, respectively.
- It added $600 unemployment insurance per week for up to four months beyond what beneficiaries normally received from states, also expanding eligibility to self-employed people and independent contractors.
- It created a $500 billion pool of taxpayer money to make loans, loan guarantees or investments to businesses, states and municipalities damaged by the crisis.
- It gave $25 billion in grants to airlines and $4 billion to cargo carriers to be used exclusively to pay employee wages, salaries, and benefits.
- It provided $17 billion in loans and loan guarantees for unspecified businesses critical to maintaining national security.
- It assigned $117 billion to hospitals and veterans' health care.
- It provided $16 billion for the strategic national stockpile of pharmaceutical and medical supplies.
- It gave $350 billion in new loans for small businesses to cover salary, wages, and benefits, with a maximum loan of $10 million.
- The stimulus provided a tax credit for retaining employees, worth up to 50 percent of wages paid during the crisis, earmarked for businesses forced to suspend operations or those who had seen gross receipts fall by 50 percent from the previous year.
- It required group health plans and insurance providers to cover preventive services related to coronavirus without cost sharing.

45

- It delayed payroll tax for employers, requiring half of the deferred tax to be paid by the end of 2021 and the other half by the end of 2022.
- It banned companies that take government loans from buying back stock until a year after the loan is paid back.
- It barred employees or executives who made at least $425,000 last year from getting a raise.
- It specifically stopped President Donald Trump and his family member's businesses from receiving emergency taxpayer relief, which was also applied to Vice President Mike Pence, heads of executive departments, members of Congress and their family members.
- It suspended federal student loan payments through September 30.

What was appropriately noticed and commented on by columnist Karen Tumulty in her *Washington Post* article dated March 27, was, "What has the right-wing pundits howling now is that $25 million for the John F. Kennedy Center for the Performing Arts was allegedly tucked into the $2.2 trillion rescue bill to deal with the coronavirus." A published challenge from Forbes, by Adam Andrzejewski, on: *Open the Books Every Dime. Online. In Real Time,* posed whether or not there was, "wasteful spending in the Coronavirus Stimulus Bill," clarifying that, "During the past ten years, the center received $68.3 million in federal grants (2010-2019). The Kennedy Center has total assets of $557 million. The Pelosi bill earmarked $35 million."

I value the Kennedy Center immensely, where the doors are currently shut due to the virus, but so are the doors to many other businesses and art centers throughout our country.

Almost as if in response to challenging Friday the thirteenth, the USA reached 83,671 cases by March 26 (an increase by 17,874 from the previous day), surpassing both China's reported 81,782 cases and Italy's 80,589 cases.

March 26: (WORLD)
Total world cases: 529,613
Deaths: 23,976
Recovered: 123,380
Active Cases: 382,257, Mild: 362,741 (95%), Critical: 19,516 (5%),
Closed: 147,356

The Dow Jones closed at 22,552.17 on March 26, 2020
The FTSE closed at 5,815.73 on March 26, 2020

I received a confirmation of receipt, thanking me for my message, on March 27. It read:

Thank you for contacting the White House. We are carefully reviewing your message.

President Donald J. Trump believes the strength of our country lies in the spirit of the American people and their willingness to stay informed and get involved. President Trump appreciates your taking the time to reach out.

For the most up-to-date information about the coronavirus, its common symptoms, and measures you can take to prevent its spread, please visit www.coronavirus.gov.

Sincerely,
The Office of Presidential Correspondence

Recognizing that this is an election year, I thought I needed to be fair, so I also wrote to the Democratic candidate, former Vice President Joe Biden, stating the same, and mentioning that I had also written to the White House. I stated my belief that he had been "strangely quiet" throughout the emerging chaos, reiterating my suggestion that this would be a way to unite the people behind a common cause in a celebration of hope whilst enduring this battle all together. I had voted for him back in the first Obama election, but not the second election. As for 2020, I am, at this particular point, uncertain.

His office, also, sent a reply, where I was asked to take a survey, and make a donation to his campaign to beat President Trump. I have since received, at the point of editing this account, 92 texts and e-mails requesting donations to defeat the President, but only one was different, which asked if I wanted to vote by a mail-in ballot.

"Panic is highly contagious, especially in situations when nothing is known and everything is in flux."

– Stephen King

"If I panic, everyone else panics."

– Kobe Bryant

CHAPTER 6
Resilience and Mental Health

So that's where we were after only a few short weeks. Our world had changed dramatically, and forever. It will never be the same. However, we will survive, so this account, despite the grimness of our new reality, is to promote resilience, and perspective while still continuing to report the ongoing reshaping of our country, and the world. As a mental health practitioner during this time of crisis, I have been confronted with fears on an astronomical level. However, I have also seen much resilience, passion, new hope and, sadly, also greed and anger, those taking advantage of the crisis.

What I have found most interesting is the initial resilience found in some of my regular patients, who originally seemed to be weathering the storm far better than new patients, who have presented only post the crisis onset, with many of the new patients having had no previous therapy, or coping tools. I have come to the probable conclusion that those who were seen earlier had already been acquiring and working on their emotional toolbox to confront their various concerns and issues, having already learned new ways to interact with others and to confront crises in their environment, learning more about "self," which includes self-esteem and self-concept, empowerment, the things "I can" do for myself – all which I believed helped these individuals to cope at the onset of the stay-at-home orders. In a very real, and possibly strange sense, previous patients were often better prepared.

I also find it interesting how those with various diagnoses were reacting to this crisis. For instance, many of those diagnosed with agoraphobia are in their happy place, and I find myself secretly grinning at the changes. Where the goal was once to help these individuals to interact more positively with their environment and to venture out, I am now telling them to stay in. Where I was once helping them to feel more comfortable with reaching out to shake the hand of or to speak with another person, I am now advising that such is no longer a good idea. No more hand shaking, and speak only whilst maintaining a six-foot distance. Where we once worked on social skills of looking people in the eyes while speaking to them, I now promote distance. If you can see their eyes well, then you are probably too close. Those with agoraphobia had this action perfected long before what I usually refer to during therapy as the "Time of COVID."

Those with OCD, standing for Obsessive Compulsive Disorder, reflect another interesting category. No self-respecting virus has a chance of survival in their homes. During the initial diagnostic interview with individuals with this disorder, I generally try to establish the degree to which their obsessive actions and thoughts impacts on their daily lives, usually starting with, "So how many times do you scrub your kitchen floor each day?" I do not believe I have ever received a response of less than 4. To these people, I am now advising them to, "Keep up the good work."

What I have also found interesting is the impact that the stay-at-home order has had on those patients who had been working on interactions with family and relationships in general. Couples, married or unmarried, who have struggled in their relationships are generally doing better. Of those couples I have been seeing to help them with their relationship, all save a few have contacted me to say that my services are no longer needed. They explain that before the stay-at-home orders, back in the "old normal," they rarely had the time to do the homework I had been giving them to address their issues, and that the previous few weeks of sharing confinement had finally given them the opportunity to pay attention and, surprise, it worked. Although it is highly unlikely that ceasing interactions with the outside world and staying confined for three weeks together will be any part of the homework I give in the "new normal" world, I can definitely see myself referencing the observations of the usual homework working better during the Time of COVID when people were desperate to find alternative ways to fill their time, desperate to share, desperate to not be alone during the crisis. In other words, make the time, and it has a much better chance of working.

It is my belief that one of the consequences of the Time of COVID will be an addition the Diagnostic and Statistical Manual (DSM), the mental health Bible. Therapy was changing almost as much as the numbers, which I checked almost daily, yet not always at the same time of the day. Where I had previously seen patients in my office, usually appropriately attired and myself generally with a suit jacket hanging on the back of my office door, I now saw (if we used FaceTime or similar) patients dressed in jeans, but with an appropriate top. The jeans could not be seen, but I judged it as inconsequential if my cat, Missie, was the only one to see my jeans beneath my desk as she curled up at my feet. As for the patients, who generally sat in a large rocking chair across from me in my office, we were now having our therapy sessions in a vast array of conditions. Some chose to walk along the beach while talking to me, where others preferred to provide me with a cooking lesson from their, now virtual, kitchen. Some would have their faces so close to the phone that only their eyes, nose and mouths could be detected, just as others might seem very far away – the new normal. Where I would once have given homework to try to go to the beach to collect pebbles or shells to externalize their issues (Object Relations), we now walked together through our phones to identify appropriate items. Where they once talked of finding cooking soothing and spoke of new recipes, we now interacted, exploring why creating made the patient feel so much more secure. It was also at this time that I began giving additional homework to my child patients – to figure out what happened to all the toilet paper...with no wrong answers.

"Although the world is full of suffering, it is also full of the overcoming of it."
– Helen Keller

CHAPTER 7
Flattening the Curve

The President was expressing his frustrations with the economic consequences and stressed the dire consequences of having millions of Americans staying at home, comparing the coronavirus to the flu, emphasizing that, "We lose thousands and thousands of people a year to the flu, we don't turn the country off every year."

President Trump tweeted that, "We can have a public health strategy that is consistent with an economic one. No one should be talking about social darwinism for the sake of the stock market."

Administration officials, sharing the President's views and eagerness to get the country back to business, began expressing their growing concerns about the escalating economic impact that the tight restrictions on movement and social interactions were having, many stating that they were worried that the White House went too far in allowing public health experts to set policy and that their actions did not need to be so draconian.

Of course, one must note that the push for Americans to stay in their homes, promoted by public health experts, was aimed at curbing the spread of the virus and "flattening the curve" of new cases with the goal of preventing the health care professionals and resources from being overwhelmed. It was noted that the officials in Italy were slow to isolate the affected regions and limit movement, leading to one of the world's worst outbreaks of Coronavirus spreading and resulting deaths.

Nevertheless, President Trump had warned that, "You are going to lose a number of people to the flu, but you are going to lose more people by putting a country into a massive recession or depression." He had added that, "You are going to have suicides by the thousands...you are going to have all sorts of things happen. You are going to have instability. You can't just come in and say let's close up the United States of America, the biggest, most successful country in the world by far."

At the same briefing, Dr. Anthony Fauci, one of the task force members, indicated that any new guidelines would not pertain to hot spots like New York, and that there could be "flexibility in different areas" based on data. "We need to know what's going on in those areas of the country where there isn't an obvious outbreak." Dr. Anthony Fauci M.D. was appointed Director of NIAID in 1984. His credits include having been the advisor to six presidents on HIV/AIDS and numerous other domestic and global health concerns. He is also credited as being a key architect of the President's Emergency Plan for AIDS relief.

Indeed, both men are right in my opinion as evidenced by a phrase I have heard numerous times over the past month, "I might lose my life to this virus, but I'll lose my life anyway if I have no means of surviving after this passes."

What I do not fully understand is why the Board of Governors of the Federal Reserve System did not shut the markets, or possibly ban short selling as, I am informed, was banned during 9/11, when the market remained closed for four straight days. Then again, we had no idea how long this crisis would last. It simply seemed like everything, absolutely everything, was suddenly unbalanced.

So we come to March 27, the day when Italy reported the highest jump in deaths for a single day, 919. This was also the day when President Trump signed a $2 trillion stimulus plan into law, representing the largest economic stimulus package in American history, which had been held up for three days. This was also the same day that BBC News in the United Kingdom announced that the British Prime Minister, Boris Johnson, had tested positive and would be self-isolating at the minister's residence in London, 10 Downing Street. By this stage, the UK had 14,543 confirmed cases, with 759 deaths.

On March 28 the CDC issued a 14-day domestic travel advisory for non-essential individuals. It stated:

Due to extensive community transmission of COVID-19 in the area, CDC urges residents of New York, New Jersey, and Connecticut to refrain from non-essential domestic travel for 14 days effective immediately. This Domestic Travel Advisory does not apply to employees of critical infrastructure industries, including but not limited to trucking, public health professionals, financial services, and food supply. These employees of critical infrastructure, as defined by the Department of Homeland Security have a special responsibility to maintain normal work schedules. The Governors of New York, New Jersey, and Connect-icut will have full discretion to implement this Domestic Travel Advisory.

At the time of the advisory, New York had reported 155 deaths, with 52,318 confirmed cases. New Jersey had reported 11,124 cases and 140 deaths.

March 28: (WORLD)
Total Cases: 617,084
Deaths: 28,376
Recovered: 137,336
Active Cases: 451,372, Mild: 427,357 (95%), Critical: 24,015 (5%),
Closed: 165,712

March 28: (USA)
Total Cases: 104,277 Deaths: 1,704
New cases: 151
Recovered: 2,525
Active Cases 100,048, Mild: 99,044, Critical: 2,494

March 29: (WORLD)
Total Cases: 679,005
Deaths: 31,771
Recovered: 146,345
Active: 500,889, Mild: 473,512 (95%), Critical: 25,377 (5%),
Closed: 178,116

March 31: (WORLD)
Total world cases: 801,064
Deaths: 38,769
Recovered 172,319
Active Cases: 589,976, Mild: 559,663 (95%), Critical: 30,313 (5%),
Closed: 211,088

March 31: (USA)
Total Cases: 164,359

Deaths: 3,173
New cases: 515
Recovered: 5,507
Active Cases: 155,679, Critical: 3,512

On March 30, Captain Brett Crozier, commanding officer of the USS Theodore Roosevelt, allegedly sent an unclassified e-mail that was leaked to the *San Francisco Chronicle*, detailing that nearly 100 sailors had tested positive on the ship.

By March 31, nearly a third of the human race was under stay-at-home or lockdown orders, which included roughly 80 percent of Americans as 30 states issued stay-at-home orders to "Flatten the Curve."

"Essential businesses," such as grocery stores were told to stay open. People were permitted to leave their home to obtain food, medicines, and essential supplies. They were allowed, even encouraged, to exercise outside, but only while maintaining a distance of at least six feet from anyone not in their own household. Some states allowed gatherings of up to 10 people.

Schools were closing along with shops, restaurants, public buildings and many services.

ANNOUNCEMENT OF STAY-AT-HOME ORDERS
Alaska: March 28 (737 people)
California: March 19 (39.6 million people)
Colorado: March 23 (5.7 million people)
Connecticut: March 23 (3.6 million people)
Hawaii: March 25 (1.4 million people)
Idaho: March 25 (1.8 million people)
Illinois: March 21 (12.7 million people)
Indiana: March 24 (6.7 million people)
Kansas: March 30 (2.9 million people)
Kentucky: March 26 (4.5 million people)
Louisiana: March 23 (4.6 million people)
Maryland: March 30 (6 million people)
Massachusetts: March 24 (6.9 million people)

Michigan: March 24 (10 million people)
Minnesota: March 27 (5.6 million people)
Montana: March 28 (1.1 million people)
New Hampshire: March 27 (1.4 million people)
New Jersey: March 21 (8.9 million people)
New Mexico: March 24 (2.1 million people)
New York: March 22 (19.5 million people)
North Carolina: March 30 (10.4 million people)
Ohio: March 23 (11.7 million people)
Oregon: March 23 (4.2 million people)
Rhode Island: March 28 (1.1 million people)
Vermont: March 25 (626,000 people)
Washington: March 23 (7.5 million people)
West Virginia: March 24 (1.8 million people)
Wisconsin: March 25 (5.8 million people)
Oklahoma: March 25 (sections varied as to the order and date, yet began in March)
Utah: March 27 (sections varied as to the order and date, yet began in March)

"Ignorance is the parent of fear."

– Herman Melville

CHAPTER 8
Month Three

The significance of April Fool's Day, April 1, was not lost on me as I looked up to the sky and wondered if this was all a bad practical joke, a comedy of errors, yet nobody was laughing. I was not laughing.

April 1: (WORLD)
Total world cases: 872,893
Deaths: 43,271
Recovered 184,588
Active cases: 645,034, Mild: 611, 590 (95%), Critical: 33,444 (5%),
Closed: 277,859

April 1: (USA)
Total Cases: 188,592 (an increase of 24,233 from last checked figures)
Deaths: 4,056
Recovered: 7,251
Active cases: 177,285, Critical: 4,576
The Dow Jones closed at 20,943.51 on April 1, 2020
The FTSE closed at 5,454.57 on April 1, 2020

There was still nothing to laugh about the next day, April 2, when it became known that 6.6 million US workers had filed their first week for unemployment benefits at the end of March. This represented the highest number of first claims in our history, with all this happening at the same time that the number of COVID cases in the world slipped into the million range, with America surpassing 200,000.

April 2 also witnessed Captain Brett Crozier of the USS Theodore Roosevelt being relieved of his command. Sailors aboard the US Navy ship cheered the Captain in support on his departure. A recommendation was later sent that he be reinstated.

On this same day, the governor of Massachusetts, Charlie Baker, tweeted his thanks to Robert and Jonathan Kraft for organizing the use of the 767 passenger plane, generally used for the New England Patriots, to transport 1.2 million N95 masks from China.

April 2: (WORLD)
Total world cases: 950,713
Deaths: 48,313
Recovered: 202,826, Active: 699,574, Mild: 663,410 (95%),
Critical: 36,164 (5%), Closed: 251,139

April 2: (USA)
Total Cases: 215,357
Deaths: 5,113
New cases: 354
Recovered: 8,878
Active Cases: 201,366, Critical: 5,005
Massachusetts: 7,738, Deaths:122
Cape Cod: 255
Texas: 4,068, Deaths: 60
New York: 83,901, Deaths: 2,219

Prior to April 3, Americans were not recommended to wear masks, unless ill or symptomatic, but this date marks the time when the American public was asked to wear either masks or non-medical face coverings such as scarves, or even shirts.

April 3: (WORLD)
Total world cases: 1,044,210
Deaths: 55,311
Recovered: 236,000, Active: 837,075, Mild: 797,476 (95%),
Critical: 39,599 (5%), Closed: 296,378
Italy: 115,242, Deaths: 13,915
China: 3,322

April 3: (USA)
Total Cases: 246,919 (increase of 31,562 from last checked figures)
Deaths: 60,378
New cases: 2,042
Recovered: 10,411
Active 230,356, Critical: 5,421
Massachusetts: 8,966, Deaths: 154
Cape Cod: 283
Texas: 4,880, Dallas: 831
New York: 93,053, Deaths: 2,538

China held a national day of mourning on Saturday, April 4, for the victims of the virus outbreak in their country. Flags flew at half-mast nationwide with a 3-minute silence tribute to express China's homage for the deaths, the victims, and martyrs of COVID-19. April 4 also represented China's Qingming Festival, which is also known as Tomb-Sweeping Day, where it is traditional for the Chinese people to pay respect to their ancestors and national heroes. Fourteen frontline workers, including "whistleblower" Doctor Li Wenliang, were honored. China had reported a total of 3,318 deaths and 81,589 confirmed COVID-19 cases two days earlier.

April 4: (WORLD)
Total world cases: 1,133,453 (increase of 89,243 since last checked figures)
Deaths: 55,311
Recovered: 222,332, Active: 766,567, Mild: 728,148 (95%),
Critical: 38,419 (5%), Closed: 277,643
Italy: 119,827, Deaths: 14,681
China: 81,639, New: 19, Deaths: 3,326
UK: 38,168, Deaths: 3,605, total per 1 mil/pop: 562, Deaths/
per 1 mil pop: 53

Italy extended its lockdown date to April 13.

April 4: (Diamond Princess Cruise Ship)
Total cases: 712
New Cases: 0
Total deaths: 11
Active cases: 82
Recovered: 619
Critical cases: 10

April 4: (USA)
Total Cases: 277,607
Deaths: 7,406 (New 8)
New cases: 446
Recovered: 12,283
Active Cases: 257,918, Critical: 5,787
Massachusetts: 10,402, Deaths: 192
Cape Cod: 314, New cases: 31, Deaths: 4
Texas: 5,669
New York: 93,053, Deaths: 2,538

An April 5 New York Times article titled: 430,000 People Have Traveled From China to US Since Coronavirus Surfaced, written by Steve Eder, Henry Fountain, Michael Keller, Muyi Xiao, and Alexandra Stevenson, reported that, "1,300 direct flights to 17 American cities had arrived in the U.S. before the President's travel restrictions." They claimed that, according to an analysis of data from both the US and China:

Since Chinese officials disclosed the outbreak of a mysterious pneumonia like illness to international health officials on New Year's Eve, at least 430,000 people have arrived in the United States on direct flights from China, including nearly 40,000 in the two months after President Trump imposed restrictions on such travel.

The article adds, *"Mr. Trump has repeatedly suggested that his travel measures impeded the virus's spread in the United States,"* quoting the President's belief that, *"I do think we were very early, but I also think that we were very smart, because we stopped China. That was probably the biggest decision we made so far."*

Their article continued:

But the analysis of the flight and other data by The New York Times shows the travel measures, however effective, may have come too late to have "kept China out," particularly in light of recent statements from health officials that as many as 25 percent of people infected with the virus may never show symptoms. Many infectious-disease experts suspect that the virus had been spreading undetected for weeks after the first American case was confirmed, in Washington State, on Jan. 20, and that it had continued to be introduced. In fact, no one knows when the virus first arrived in the United States.

During the first half of January, when Chinese officials were underplaying the severity of the outbreak, no travelers from China were screened for potential exposure to the virus. Health screening began in mid-January, but only for a number of travelers who had been in Wuhan and only at the airports in Los Angeles, San Francisco and New York. By that time, about 4,000 people had already entered the United States directly from Wuhan, according to VariFlight, an aviation data company based in China. The measures were expanded to all passengers from China two weeks later.

It was certainly recognized that the President's decision to impose travel restrictions met with significant resistance, especially during a time when the World Health Organization (WHO) was not giving this advice. Once again, it was an election year, and I, as a mere American citizen subjected to a barrage of information and frequently conflicting information, found myself occasionally feeling like some of my patients, overwhelmed and somewhat fearful. The lives of absolutely everyone were at risk, and I often felt that the virus was being weaponized for political purposes while the American people were the pawns in a highly charged situation. "He closed the country too soon." "He closed the country too late." Contradictions were rampant and seemed to alter almost daily and as per the topic being discussed. President Trump's actions initially attracted suggestions and accusations of appearing to be discriminatory, or xenophobic. Such claims were soon to change.

"I do not want to be a pawn in a political campaign."

– General Herbert Norman Schwarzkopf Jr.

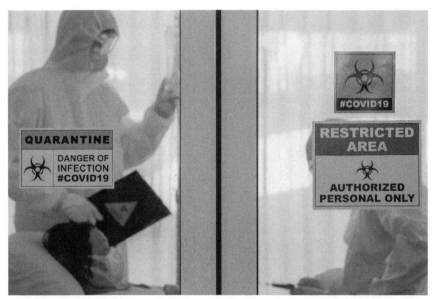

Hospital "essential" workers around the world scrambled during the Pandemic of 2020 to battle COVID-19.

Panic buying begins almost immediately for staple needs. Many things, such as hand sanitizer, Lysol or similar, and toilet paper seemed to almost disappear from the shelves.

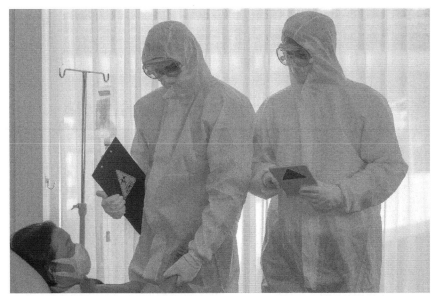

Medical staff try to offer hope while the hopes of many are challenged.

Many foods become scarce as supplies were strained.

Facilities, amenities, daycares, schools, gyms, spas, restaurants, bars, libraries, museums, court houses, states and nations began to close.

Travel and movements were increasingly restricted.

Various teams throughout the world were strategizing for battle.

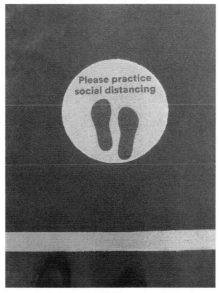

We learned a new term – "Social Distancing."

We also learned new ways to be safe and to interact.

Our existence as a social species is challenged.

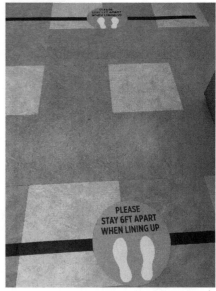

*We were reminded of the crisis everywhere we turned
and in almost everything we heard and did.*

The stock market seemed to also suffer from a virus.

*Earlier than most expected, we started
to find ways to begin flattening the curve.*

We were beginning to fight back, but at a very high cost.

*Entering Phase I of the end of the Stay at Home Orders,
the End of the Beginning, looked different in different areas
of the country, yet it proved that mankind could adapt, we could
survive, we had the capacity and the strength to change in order
to save our way of life as much as possible in the New Abnormally Normal.*

CHAPTER 9
Immunity, Isolation, Perspective, and Reset

The initial stay-at-home advice as per the telehealth ability was well over two weeks earlier by this stage. I had made my preparations in a manner one might prepare for camp. When our director asked about the sudden absence of toilet paper from the shelves, I realized that I had not been shopping for groceries for nearly a week. I knew that officials were advising us to be aware that there were many who were asymptomatic, yet still contagious, and that symptoms might not appear until 2-14 days after exposure. In other words, one might have the virus and be unaware of it, or the person in front of you might have the virus and neither one of you would be aware of it. I anticipated, and tried to prepare my patients for being in our homes at least until the middle of May.

First on my list was hand sanitizer. I had the one from my office, and two at home, but I suspected that I would be using it far more regularly for a while, so I searched. Everyone was out of stock, so I needed to think outside the box, and try to do so quicker than those clearly already ahead of me. I also wanted to find some for my son and his family, and for my daughter in the hope that I could send it to her in Dallas, Texas. It seemed that none had yet thought to check out stores with travel supplies, so I found six small-sized Purell bottles in the travel section of Bed Bath and Beyond.

Next was the toilet paper, which I found in the more remote shops along with a few boxes of tissues. Armed with these in my cart, I went in search of milk, both fresh and powdered. There were two medium-sized bags of powdered milk left on the shelf. I confess that I took both, then stopped when I turned and saw another woman walking up the aisle in search of the same. I handed her one, inwardly thinking and actually stating openly to her that, "We need to keep our humanity." She expressed no appreciation whatsoever and simply stomped off with her treasure...so much for humanity. I could feel myself slipping deeper and deeper into a new world.

I decided that I needed to assess all available information to further prepare myself. I discovered new rules that would guide my daily life:

Death Rate of COVID-19 on surfaces – how long it can survive:

- Up to 24 hours on cardboard
- Up to 3 days on stainless steel
- Up to 4 hours on copper
- Up to 24 hours on cardboard
- Up to 3 hours in air particles called aerosols
- Most material I could find indicated, but did not confirm, that I did not need to worry much about the virus living on hair.

It had been recommended to clean and disinfect surfaces you touch frequently, like doorknobs, drawers, handles, and light switches and to wear disposable gloves when handling dirty laundry, to not shake laundry, and to clean and disinfect laundry hampers.

At the time of writing this, there is no evidence indicative of contracting COVID-19 from food, as this virus does not seem to be like a norovirus, or hepatitis A, which are two food-borne stomach viruses. Nevertheless, it has been recommended to wash one's hands with soap and water for at least 20 seconds before preparing or eating food, rinse food and vegetables before eating, wiping the can lids before opening and to dedicate one cutting board for raw foods only.

My patients with OCD would be so incredibly proud of me.

My initial task on returning home was to check my supplies in my basement storage, having an eerie sense as I thought of my preparations made several months earlier. I was prepared, but what had I missed? I had not thought of the toilet paper and hand sanitizer, but what else? I made my list and returned to the store to purchase plastic baggies, trash bags, two laundry detergents, four dish soaps, three hand soaps, enough dog and cat food for two months, fresh veggies, water, fish, and meat. Returning home, I sectioned the fish and meats into portions, placing them into the baggies and dating them before freezing. I did the same with the vegetables. Everything was washed first.

I did not purchase paper towels, as I confess that I have never understood people's preference for using a paper towel to clean a surface. I rotate my towels, purchasing a few new dish towels every few months, rotating the old towels for lesser purposes than using for dishes and hands, simply washing them before reuse. These were now all placed together into a container for clean towels whereby each could be used once and then sent straight to washing, eliminating the need for costly paper towels.

Beyond the use of towels, I made a battle plan with a goal to learn as much as I could to protect myself, my family, friends, and patients. Sheets would be removed daily and exchanged for clean ones for the next night. Shoes would be left just inside the door, which was an action I always tried to do anyway, but I was now denying myself the opportunity to cheat. Two more bottles of hand sanitizer, a box of masks, and another box of gloves were ordered online. I already had a pulse oximeter and thermometers in my First Aid kit along with general cold and flu treatments. I also had prescription medicines from my arsenal due to previous extensive travel, where excursions usually all went very well, yet with two exceptions. I had learned, perhaps the hard way, to always have meds on hand if needed after contracting Cholera while in India in the 1980s, and SARS whilst in China during their outbreak. I had returned to London from China as I began to feel unwell, innocently thinking that, *I might be coming down with a cold.* I was feeling a little worse when we reached Hong Kong, and then felt terrible on the flight to London, having already made an appointment with my doctor in the United Kingdom for the next day. I went to that appointment, explaining that I had suffered several hours of having difficulty breathing and fever while on the flight, but that I was beginning to feel better, asking if I might have had a brief case of pneumonia. His response was that, "You have SARS." My reply was, "Never heard of it. Is that worse than pneumonia?" Little did I know! I had been in China for over two weeks, and I had heard nothing whatsoever. Indeed, I had seen a doctor at the end of my trip before leaving. He handed me a plastic bottle, which I still have, with instructions to take five of the pills every three hours. The pills, most which I still have, look much like rabbit droppings, although I happily have no basis on which to compare the taste.

Anyway, I was making my preparations, filling my car with gas, and promising myself to keep it nearly full in anticipation of a shortage if the trucks stopped transportation. I had purchased two boxes of Q-tips, one for the kitchen and the other for the master bedroom and bath for any needs to touch my face after the public was informed that this respiratory virus was transmitted through droplets, and therefore one should avoid touching their face. An article by Kwok, YL, Gralton, J, and McLaws, ML in the 2015 *Am J Infect Control*, titled: Face Touching: a Frequent Habit That Has Implications for Hand Hygiene, expounded on a study involving 26 medical students at the University of New South Wales, focusing on their face-touching behavior, especially with regard to hand-to-face touching the mucosal or non-mucosal areas. Their conclusion was that each of the 26 students touched their face at least 23 times each hour. The Q-tips were intended to address any unwanted facial itch.

Next was to arm myself with information. In the land of the "normal," I would watch the news at least once each morning and then before going to bed, often also checking out the BBC, the latter which was a habit formed after living in England for so many decades. Now the news and the Internet became my means of educating myself to maintain safety. This is something I had done with patients over the years when they had a question about housing, certain plants or foods, customs, treatments, any number of things where I would resort to, "So why don't we check out the University of Google to see what we can learn about your question?" This time, it was my question.

Having trained and worked as a nurse during my personal ancient history, I already knew that there are many different kinds of viruses, yet researchers are working hard at the time of writing this account to learn all they can about this particular coronavirus. We have learned that this new coronavirus is spread through droplets released into the air when an infected person coughs or sneezes, possibly even when the person speaks. However, droplets generally do not travel more than a few feet, usually falling onto the ground or onto surfaces, explaining why social distancing is such a good protective measure to control the spread.

The symptoms of this particular virus included shortness of breath, cough, fever, sore throat, diarrhea, headache, muscle aches and pains, with many victims also reporting a loss of smell and taste. This was a virus that could lead to severe respiratory problems, kidney failure and, sadly, even death.

I knew that coronaviruses are fairly common in different animals and, rarely, that an animal coronavirus could infect humans. I was also aware that coronaviruses are named for their appearance as, under a microscope, the virus looks as if it is covered with pointed areas that resemble a crown. But why was it that common soap was so effective in killing this virus?

I found a very informative answer in a New York Times article dated March 13, 2020, written by Ferris Jabr, who explained in his article titled: Why Soap Works, and subtitled: At the molecular level, soap breaks things apart. At the level of society, it helps hold everything together. Jabr explained that:

Soap is made of pin-shaped molecules, each of which has a hydrophilic head — it readily bonds with water — and a hydrophobic tail, which shuns water and prefers to link up with oils and fats. These molecules, when suspended in water, alternately float about as solitary units, interact with other molecules in the solution and assemble themselves into little bubbles called micelles, with heads pointing outward and tails tucked inside.

The article further explained that:

Some bacteria and viruses have lipid membranes that resemble double-layered micelles with two bands of hydrophobic tails sandwiched between two rings of hydrophilic heads. These membranes are studded with important proteins that allow viruses to infect cells and perform vital tasks that keep bacteria alive. Pathogens wrapped in lipid membranes include coronaviruses, H.I.V., the viruses that cause hepatitis B and C, herpes, Ebola, Zika, dengue, and numerous bacteria that attack the intestines and respiratory tract.

Jabr reported that:

When you wash your hands with soap and water, you surround any microorganisms on your skin with soap molecules. The hydrophobic tails of the free-floating soap molecules attempt to evade water; in the process, they wedge themselves into the lipid envelopes of certain microbes and viruses, prying them apart," which makes the, "Essential proteins spill from the ruptured membranes into the surrounding water, killing the bacteria and rendering the viruses useless.

Although authorities claim that soap is a very effective viral weapon, panic buying resulted in hand sanitizers and bleach flying off the shelves, despite many resorting to hand sanitizers that lacked the claimed necessary minimum of 60 percent alcohol. Pictures and news footage showed many countries resorting to men in hazmat suits spraying bleach products onto streets and structures, yet one can only wonder as to the long-term impact of exposure to bleach if inhaled too much and over a long period of time.

It became known that the prime means of contracting the virus was from person-to-person transmission, from being too close to an infected individual, or from shaking hands with an infected person. We had been taught since childhood how to politely shake another person's hand on greeting, but our social norms were changing rapidly.

So, I had my home plan. I would try to help my patients during the day via telehealth whilst remaining in my home with the exception of walks, and occasional drives to the beach or around town where the streets were mostly empty, driving over to park along the beach to watch the ocean waves. I would collect my mail with gloves, place the mail into a paper shopping bag, and then leave it to set for 24 hours for any possible infection to die off on the paper, with plastic abandoned on my library floor for four days, removing the gloves and placing them into the wash. Then I chose a time once every 7-10 days to refresh perishables such as lettuce, which I learned does not respond well to freezing. Each time I went out and returned meant that I would need to "RESET" my "wait to see" clock, waiting 2-14 days to see if I developed symptoms as a result of my excursion into the battlegrounds. My contact with the outside world was through my phone and television, interacting only with Mia and Missie. Such was my new, hopefully temporary, new normal, yet I was not totally isolated.

The phone allowed me to speak with friends, family, neighbors, and an escalating caseload of mental health patients. However, I was now entering nearly a month in confinement. I had been to the store twice. The first time was grim with empty shelves and tape with arrows along the floor to tell me which way to walk. I gathered a few things and went to the register where neither the cashier nor the bagger wore gloves or masks. I did ask. The cashier simply reached into a drawer and put on his gloves. The grocery bagger responded with, "I left them in the car, and I haven't had the time to get them out yet." On returning home, having been careful to remove my gloves before entering my car and then removing my shoes at my entrance, I heard from a neighbor that a teacher at one of the schools had reopened the premises on the basis that she wanted,

"Only two hours to review projects with the students." It was obvious that the stay-at-home orders would be lifted later rather than sooner.

RESET

I went out again the following week. This time, the cashier had donned gloves and mask, but not the bagger, who responded that, "I don't like the gloves because they don't fit right." Worse, another cashier wore both gloves and mask, but she covered only her mouth, with a rather large schnoz hanging over the top of the mask. I mentioned it again, and was ignored. As if a bad omen for the future, a fight was erupting at the self-service area, where a man had, presumably accidentally, pushed his cart into the woman before him. She demanded that he maintain the six-foot social distancing. His replies were rude and the woman's, presumably husband, started yelling at the man, which resulted in a brawl on the floor. I left and entered my car, watching the two men also leave, where the first man went to his own vehicle, and the second man went first to his car, then removed a crowbar that he took and threw into the windscreen of the other man's vehicle. Going out to buy lettuce was certainly not what it used to be. The abnormal was definitely becoming the new normal.

RESET

Clinicians are not exempt from anxiety and depression. Unfortunately, we do not complete all of our education, training and internships and emerge not only with a qualification, but also with an exemption card. Indeed, we often feel triggered, and I was beginning to realize that I needed to take my own advice. I was emphasizing to patients the need to maintain self-care, trying to instill empowerment to survive this pandemic and to emerge a better and more informed self. I tried to keep them occupied while they were confined at home, exploring projects to fill their newly acquired free time, interjecting "Time Management" into their Care Plans, which was different and tailored for each. Some began family nights, home movie nights, meal times with themes, journaling their time during confinement, costume day, stepping up the pace of homework.

But what about me? I was isolated away from my family, resorting to phone calls and PhotoCircles to spy on my grandson's progress. My savings and investments were disappearing at the same time that I was working overtime. Indeed, it was no surprise to learn that our numbers had increased by 25 percent for mental health sessions during this crisis. None of us complained. This is what we do. But I found myself with a need to address "self," so after the shelves were stocked, I made personal plans.

My personal tailored and self-imposed Care Plan also consisted of several aspects I imposed on patients: eating healthy foods, exercise, and meditation. My friends checked in by phone almost daily, colleagues frequently, and I contacted my children at least weekly. I regard Mia and Missie as a part of my family, but they were previously less involved with my professional life. Now, when a patient introduced me to (names changed) cat Jasper, dog Fido, a chameleon, snake or similar, I would introduce them to Mia and Missie. When someone was crying or upset, I could now introduce Mia or Missie up for FaceTime Animal Therapy.

Missie experienced no real changes to her life with the pandemic. She still gravitated from one warm place to sleep to another, alternating with looking out at the lake to spy on the ducks and the geese. Mia was different, and she was beginning to look at me with the "Am I being punished?" stare. In the old "normal," she would go to doggy-daycare roughly four days weekly when I had patients all day. Now she was at home with me, and we were both trying to adapt. Therefore, she was included in my regiment: teach her to better loose-leash walk, and also to fetch her leash when she needed to go out to acquire her North-South Axis. We also worked on her sharing a meal with me, utilizing a small table for her, complete with cloth under her plate, to eat her meals and, in my maniacal need to find distraction, teaching her to take my clothes down to the washing machine. In the old normal, I would often be greeted with piles of my clothes before the door on my return when she had not needed to have daycare. The vet explained that, "She just wants little piles of you." This became a problem with doggy-drool, so in the Time of COVID, I taught her to take the clothes to the washing machine…so much was the desperation for distraction. She was learning new tasks to fill her time. As for me, I decided to write a book – this account.

I was seeing more New York and New Jersey car plates in the area as I continued to work from my home in Massachusetts. More alarming to me was that

PANDEMIC 2020

I was beginning to feel increasingly more like one of my patients as I worried about the economy, the growing numbers of those infected, the safety of my patients, and my family. I was missing visits with my son and his family, and my grandson, Nathan, was changing daily. Nathan was only three months old when I last saw him before I closed my personal social door to the world. Now he was five months old. I would hear him trying to form his first words on the other end of the phone and share FaceTime with the family, yet I longed to hold them and show my love. Then again, we can no longer do that. It seemed to have become improper to come too close, to shake hands, to hug, to caress, to kiss someone you love.

It was originally thought, and spoken about in light jest that the stay-at-home orders would result in a baby boom, where the resulting generation would be referred to as "COVID Babies" or "Coronials", and then we started to be warned about the dangers associated with sexual relationships as new information about COVID-19 became known. We had closed out the month of March with numerous advisories, but I believe the one presented to me for discussion regarding a NYC.gov release really said it all:

NYC Health: Sex and Coronavirus Disease 2019 (COVID-19)

All New Yorkers should stay home and minimize contact with others to reduce the spread of COVID-19.

But can you have sex?

Here are some tips for how to enjoy sex and to avoid spreading COVID-19.

1. Know how COVID-19 spreads.
   - You can get COVID-19 from a person who has it.
     The virus can spread to people who are within about 6 feet of a person with COVID-19 when that person coughs or sneezes.
     The virus can spread through direct contact with their saliva or mucus.
   - We still have a lot to learn about COVID-19 and sex.
   COVID-19 has been found in feces of people who are infected with the virus. COVID-19 has not yet been found in semen or vaginal fluid. We know that other coronaviruses do not efficiently transmit through sex.

2. Have sex with people close to you.
    - You are your safest sex partner. Masturbation will not spread COVID-19, especially if you wash your hands (and any sex toys) with soap and water for at least 20 seconds before and after sex.
    - The next safest partner is someone you live with. Having close contact — including sex — with only a small circle of people helps prevent spreading COVID-19. Have sex only with consenting partners.
    - You should avoid close contact — including sex — with anyone outside your household. If you do have sex with others, have as few partners as possible.
    - If you usually meet your sex partners online or make a living by having sex, consider taking a break from in-person dates. Video dates, sexting, or chat rooms may be options for you.
3. Take care during sex.
    - Kissing can easily pass COVID-19. Avoid kissing anyone who is not part of your small circle of close contacts.
    - Rimming (mouth on anus) might spread COVID-19. Virus in feces may enter your mouth.
    - Condoms and dental dams can reduce contact with saliva or feces, especially during oral or anal sex.
    - Washing up before and after sex is more important than ever. Wash hands often with soap and water for at least 20 seconds. Wash sex toys with soap and warm water.
    - Disinfect keyboards and touch screens that you share with others (for video chat, for watching pornography or for anything else).
4. Skip sex if you or your partner is not feeling well.
    - If you or a partner may have COVID-19, avoid sex and especially kissing.
    - If you start to feel unwell, you may be about to develop symptoms of COVID-19, which include fever, cough, sore throat, or shortness of breath.

- If you or your partner has a medical condition that can lead to more severe COVID-19, you may also want to skip sex. Medical conditions include lung disease, heart disease, diabetes, cancer or a weakened immune system (for example, having unsuppressed HIV and a low CD4 count).

5. Prevent HIV, other sexually transmitted infections (STIs) and unplanned pregnancy.

    - HIV: Condoms, pre-exposure prophylaxis (PrEP) and having an undetectable viral load all help prevent HIV. For more information, visit nyc.gov/health and search HIV.
    - Other STIs: Condoms help prevent other STIs.
      Visit nyc.gov/health and search STIs.
    - Pregnancy: Make sure you have an effective form of birth control for the coming weeks.

    Visit nyc.gov/health and search birth control.

For the latest information, visit nyc.gov/coronavirus or cdc.gov/covid19. For real-time updates, text "COVID" to 692-692. Messages and data rates may apply.

REF: The NYC Health Department may change recommendations as the situation evolves. 3.27.20

When challenged for my opinion, my response was, "Terrific, now COVID-19 is an STD." This made me assume that perhaps the original predictions of a baby boom might have been slightly overestimated. It was an interesting conversation to say the least, as the abnormal was ever-becoming the new normal.

What was also growing more alarming as the Time of COVID slipped into April was a growing sense of inner alarm as I learned that many elective surgeries and non-COVID treatments had been either cancelled or rescheduled, and I became very concerned when I learned of those not receiving their regular dialysis treatments, and others not receiving previously scheduled chemo and/or radiation treatments. I also heard of two cases where an individual suffering from severe abdominal pain waited days for an appendectomy – complete with treatment for the resulting peritonitis. It seemed as if everything "regular" was moved out of the way. I understood the rescheduling of procedures such as face-lifts and similar minor treatments, but even rescheduling surgeries for rotator cuff tears was leaving patients in prolonged pain. I do not wish to minimize the need to address those patients and families dealing with the virus, and there was certainly no question that we all needed to do our part in "flattening the curve," but I once again found myself urging perspective. I looked down at my hands. Two weeks earlier, I had decided to use only soap instead of hand sanitizer, which seemed to have damaged the natural oils in my skin to the point of them becoming cracked and blistered. They were looking better after weeks of applying coconut oil and creams...such was life in the new normal where the "regular" seemed to be on the retreat.

According to a *Medscape* article dated July 23, 2019 by Brian Daley MD, MBA, FACS, FCCP, CNSC and editor Roy Praveen MD:

In severe intra-abdominal infections and peritonitis, the mortality rate may increase to greater than 30-50%. The concurrent development of sepsis, SIRS, and MOF can increase the mortality rate to greater than 70%, and, in these patients, more than 80% of deaths occur with an active infection present.

According to a CJASN article in 2015 titled: CKD in Elderly Patients Managed without Dialysis: Survival, Symptoms, and Quality of Life, by Mark Brown, Gemma Collett, Elizabeth Josland, Celine Foote, Quiang Li and Frank Brennan, the survival rates of those with Chronic Kidney Disease (CKD) not having dialysis bore the conclusion that:

Elderly patients who choose not to have dialysis as part of shared decision making survive a median of 16 months and about one-third survive 12 months past a time when dialysis might have otherwise been indicated. Utilizing the skills of palliative medicine helps provide reasonable symptom control and QOL without dialysis.

"QOL" is indicative of quality of life.

Finally, an NIH: National Cancer Institute, February 26, 2016 release, by "NCI staff" titled, Missed Radiation Therapy Sessions Increase Risk of Cancer Recurrence, advised that:

Patients who miss radiation therapy sessions during cancer treatment have an increased risk of their disease returning, even if they eventually complete their course of radiation treatment, according to a new study.

The magnitude of the effect was higher than the researchers anticipated, which they believed suggested that noncompliance with radiation therapy may be an indicator for other risk factors that could negatively affect out- comes. The NIH staff reference that their announcement was based on, "The study appeared January 30 in the International Journal of Radiation Oncology • Biology • Physics."

The reason for my growing concern for these individuals was that the cancellations and delays in their non-COVID treatment was potentially placing them at greater risk as they were also battling with medical issues often with higher risks and mortality rates. I have no intention of minimizing, but one death from a lack of much-needed dialysis is too many, just as one death from a lack of chemo and radiation treatment is too many, and equally that one death from a lack of treatment for COVID-19 is too many. Nevertheless, it was being widely circulated that the vast majority of those who contracted COVID-19 had mild cases. Of course, the mortality rate was, and will continue to be constantly changing until this is all over. The situation is still fluid. COVID-19 was dumped on humanity without any serious warning, and our initial reactions were one of alarm, fear, panic and even hysteria. Everyone scrambled in their various fields as we raced to catch up with the virus in a frenzied attempt to contain, then mitigate, the damage. To a large extent, I believe that it was only when we finally did manage, very recently, to mitigate, to get ahead of the damage, and push the curve down, that we were able to look back at what we missed. The learning curve for addressing the crisis was as steep as the influx of new cases and deaths, with the ponderously slow trickle down the other side of the mountain that allowed everyone to look back and see what was missed, what was learned, with time to breathe again while trying frantically to figure out the next step before it could surge ahead of us again. Each profession, whether government, utilities and other services, medical and related fields, schools...all had their areas to address to assess the damage, and to adjust their various commitments as the abnormal continued to shift into the new normal.

PERSPECTIVE

85

April 5: (WORLD)
Total world cases: 1,236,296
Deaths: 67,231
Recovered: 255,606
Active cases: 913,459, Mild: 868,492 (95%), Critical: 44,967 (5%),
Closed: 322,837
Italy: 124,632, Deaths: 15,362
China: 81,669, New: 30, Deaths: 3,329
UK: 47,806; Deaths, 4,934, Active Cases: 42,737

April 5: (USA)
Total cases: 321,423 (increase of 43,816 from day beforehand)
Deaths: 9,129, (increase of 1,723 from day beforehand))
New cases: 10,066
Recovered: 16,570
Active cases: 295,724, Critical: 8,468
Massachusetts: not updated
Cape Cod: 330, New cases: 16, Deaths: 4
Texas: not updated
Louisiana: 4,587, Deaths: 91

By April 5, over 10 million Americans had filed for unemployment. This was the same day that a tiger tested positive for the virus at the Bronx Zoo in New York.

"Too much self-centered attitude, you see, brings, you see, isolation. Result: loneliness, fear, anger. The extreme self-centered attitude is the source of suffering."

– Dalai Lama

"I believe everyone should have a broad picture of how the universe operates and our place in it. It is a basic human desire. And it also puts our worries in perspective."

– Stephen Hawking

CHAPTER 10
But Can I Pay My Bills?

My patients usually commenced our session by expelling newly acquired fears from news headlines, fearful of the next day, the next headline, the next hour. Would they be able to pay their bills, would their current benefits continue, would they survive, what could they do to remain safe? Indeed, conversations with neighbors and friends had also changed, and were now often commencing in the same manner. I would remind them that there were no real guidelines of how to deal with this. Of course, there were certainly emergency guidelines and plans, but never before in American history had we simply turned the country "off"; we were learning new things about what was often referred to as the Silent Enemy every day to try to understand that, initially, it was like trying to put out a fire in a haystack, but to please maintain perspective – this would, most definitely, end. This was a temporary situation, and to remember that the last publicized pandemic, over a century earlier, did not benefit as much from what we have today where the science is better. Healthcare is also better, and we have much greater means at our disposal to combat the virus. I would remind them of calming skills, and that Social Distancing had already proven to be effective, to wear their gloves and masks, address self-care – and they should get through this, also pointing out that, even though the numbers of those infected was growing, that the numbers of those recovering was also growing daily. Indeed, I would tell them that we were actually lucky and should be grateful that the mortality rate was so low, that another contagion might have been much worse, and that the numbers, as horrible as they were, would change. They had to change, that eventually the numbers would switch places as the number of those recovered were destined to surpass the number of those dying, that by the very nature of the manner this virus was behaving, that the numbers had to change – eventually. My additional and increasingly delivered advice to many was simply to turn their televisions off, unless they could find something comforting to view beyond the news that fueled their tensions. Viewer availability also seemed to change with one channel devoting entire days to single themes, such as *Homecoming Revenge*, followed by *Death of a Cheerleader*, followed by *The Secret Lives of Cheerleaders*, followed by *Identity Theft of a Cheerleader*, after which the viewer might watch *Homekilling Queen*. As for movies, the primary selection promoted on my screen to watch included titles such as *Survive the Night, Contagion, Pandemic, Global Meltdown, Earthquake, City on Fire, After Darkness, and The End of the World*. I have no doubt these are outstanding shows, yet the circumstances made these seem overwhelming, at least to me. I advised patients to simply go out for a long walk in the sunshine...of course, wearing their mask and gloves... and to maintain social distancing.

Also on April 5, the BBC announced that the Prime Minister of the United Kingdom, Boris Johnson, had been admitted to the hospital. This announcement came 10 days after he had tested positive, although Downing Street made it known that this was merely a "precautionary" move, the announcement coinciding with Queen Elizabeth II addressing her nation, and its people.

Having lived in the UK for nearly four decades, splitting much of my time flying between the shores of the US and the UK, I had formed a fond respect for this 94-year-old woman who succeeded her father, King George VI, in 1952. I have watched her face adversities and criticism with dignity, compassion and respect for her people. In recent years, she has refrained from numerous public addresses, beyond heartfelt Christmas wishes, which my children would always watch, yet she spoke to provide reassurance and hope once again to her people on April 5, 2020.

She commenced her speech with:

I'm speaking to you at what I know is an increasingly challenging time, a time of disruption in the life of our country, a disruption that has brought grief to some, financial difficulties to many, and enormous changes to the daily lives of us all.

She reminded her people to "remain resolute," expressing her hope that:

Those who come after us will say the Britons of this generation were as strong as any, that the attributes of self-discipline, of quiet, good-humored resolve, and of fellow feeling still characterize this country.

She concluded with:

We should take comfort that while we may have more still to endure, better days will return. We will be with our friends again. We will be with our families again. We will meet again. But for now, I send my thanks and warmest good wishes to you all.

April 6: (WORLD)

Total world cases: 1,284,740 (increase of 48,444 from the day beforehand)

Deaths: 70,320 (increase of 3,089)

Recovered: 271,731 (increase of 16,125)

Active Cases: 942,689, Mild: 896,695 (95%), Critical: 45,994 (5%),

Closed: 342,051

Italy: 128,948

Spain: 135,032

China: not updated

UK: not updated

April 6: (USA)

Total cases: 336,851(increase of 15,428 from the day beforehand)

Deaths: 9,620

New cases: 178

Recovered: 17,977

Active Cases: 309,254, Critical: 8,702

Massachusetts; 12,500, Deaths: 231

Cape Cod: 347

Texas: 6,812

New York: 122,911

On April 7, it was announced that the 55-year-old Prime Minister, Boris Johnson, was moved to intensive care.

The next day, April 8, 2020, China announced that it was lifting its 76-day lockdown of Wuhan. We had a time frame, but not everyone trusted the facts and figures coming out of China.

The Dow Jones closed at 22,653.86 on April 7, 2020.
The FTSE closed at 5,704.45 on April 7, 2020.

Vermont senator, Bernie Sanders, bowed out of the 2020 Presidential campaign on April 8 as a Democratic candidate, ending the split in his party and clearing the way for his opponent, former Vice President Joe Biden, to be the Democratic nominee. Both presidential candidates entered this stage of their campaigns with difficulties. Biden would have difficulties campaigning and meeting with voters during the stay-at-home orders and restrictions. President Trump was busy waging a very important war against a virus that was decimating the economy he had worked so hard to build and which had, only a few months previously, been one of the cornerstones of his campaign. In addition, the President still had the ever-present few key Democrats chomping at his heels in what seemed to be an emerging pattern. Americans spent years witnessing the threats to impeach, even before the President was elected, yet there was no sign of relief after the impeachment had failed, only a sense of dread with the anticipation. What would be next? After all, this was an election year.

By April 10, New York alone had more virus cases than any other country. There were 466,299 confirmed cases nationwide, with roughly 162,000 in New York. More states had issued stay-at-home orders as unemployment numbers soared. Each state had different issues to confront and ways to meet the challenge, such as New Mexico reportedly using cell phone data to verify if their residents were maintaining social distancing, and some states requesting those with vacation or second homes in their areas to please stay away. More important, several states were reporting difficulties with obtaining vital essentials such as PPEs, expressing their belief that they were battling each other, and the federal government, competing with one another for essentials, often resulting in escalating prices. Governor Cuomo from New York was one of the first to suggest a multi-state consortium to address the competition and in an effort to increase their purchasing power, resulting in the seven-state New England Consortium.

During one of his daily virus press briefings aired on CNN, the 62-year-old former Attorney General of New York and Governor since 2010, explained that, "On purchasing, you can't have a situation where 50 states are competing with each other to buy the same material; that is what is happening now," clarifying that, "We're literally bidding up the prices ourselves." He was very correct in his repeated insistence that such was, "Not the way to do business."

There was a spark of relief on this day in April when Russia and Saudi Arabia agreed to end their price war to help stabilize the global oil market. An OPEC meeting was reportedly held via a video call, which resulted in a proposed deal amongst producers to slash production of crude by 10 million barrels per day during the months of May and June.

The deal was solidified a few days later, following nearly a week of phone calls. President Trump later praised the deal on twitter, stating that it, "will save hundreds of thousands of energy jobs in the United States."

April 10: (WORLD)
Total world cases: 1,621,348 (increase of 85,477 from the day beforehand)
Deaths: 100,268 (increase of 10,395 from the day before)
Recovered: 369,646, Active: 1,177,982, ; Mild: 1,127,936 (96%),
Critical: 50,046 (4%), Closed: 469,914
Italy: 147,577, Deaths: 18,849
China: 81,907, New: 42, Deaths: 3,336

April 10: (USA)
Total cases: 478,366 (an increase of 43,199 from the day beforehand)
Deaths: 17,927
New Cases: 9,800
Recovered: 26,163
Active cases: 434,276, Critical: 10,896

The United Kingdom's Prime Minister, Boris Johnson, was discharged from St. Thomas' hospital on April 12, accompanied by the following Associated Press announcement:

On the advice of his medical team, the P.M. will not be immediately return-ing to work. He wishes to thank everybody at St. Thomas' for the brilliant care he has received.

91

On April 14, President Trump announced that he was halting US funding to the World Health Organization, requesting a review of the WHO's, "role in severely mismanaging and covering up the spread of coronavirus." Also on April 14, Austria became one of the first European countries to loosen its lockdown orders, becoming another petri dish. Would they be able to open safely? What would happen?

April 14: (WORLD)
Total world cases: 1,990,983 (increase of 128,718 from the daybeforehand)
Deaths: 125,934 (increase of 10,954 from the day beforehand)
Recovered: 466,997 (increase of 35,324 from the day beforehand)
Active Cases: 1,398,052, Mild: 1,346,491 (96%), Critical: 38,419 (5%),
Closed: 592,931
Italy: 162,448, New cases: 2,972, Deaths: 21,067, Deaths per 1 mil pop: 348
China: 82,249, New 89, Deaths: 3,341
UK: 93,873, Deaths: 1,207, Deaths/per mil pop: 178
Italy: 162,448, New cases: 2,972, Deaths: 21,067

April 14: (Diamond Princess – the same as April 4)

April 14: (USA)
Total cases: 610,467 (an increase of 50,034 from the day beforehand)
Deaths: 25,854 (an increase of 3,739 from the day beforehand)
Recovered: 38,520
Active cases: 546,093, Critical: 13,438
Massachusetts: 26,867, New cases: 844
Cape Cod: 514, New cases: 12, Deaths: 17
Texas: 5,669
New York: (no update on numbers), Deaths: 10,834
The Dow Jones closed at 23,949.76 on April 14, 2020.
The FTSE closed at 5,791.31 on April 14, 2020.

More states issued Stay-at-Home orders in April:
Alabama: April 4 (4.9 people)
District of Columbia: April 1 (roughly 700,000 people)
Florida: April 3 (21.5 million people)
Georgia: April 3 (10.6 million people)
Maine: April 2 (1.3 million people)
Mississippi: April 3 (roughly 3 million people)
Missouri: April 6 (roughly 6 million people)
Nevada: April 1 (roughly 3 million people)
Pennsylvania: April 1 (12.8 million people)
South Carolina: April 7 (roughly 5 million people)
Texas: April 2 (nearly 30 million people)

By April 16, 22 million Americans had filed for unemployment.

"POLITICS, n. A strife of interests masquerading as a contest of principles. The conduct of public affairs for private advantage."
                    – Ambrose Bierce, The Unabridged Devil's Dictionary

CHAPTER 11
New York

I do not believe that anyone was surprised that New York became the epicenter in the United States. This state had its first confirmed case on March 1, yet it was widely anticipated at the time that the numbers were already much higher as the population, particularly in the densely occupied main cities, tried to brace themselves for what was to come.

Their first case was reportedly a 39-year-old healthcare worker who was a resident of Manhattan, returning to New York on February 25. She had recently traveled from Iran. The second confirmed case in New York arose the next day, an attorney who worked in Manhattan, also representing the first case of community spread, as he had not recently traveled abroad.

By March 4, nine of those who had contact with the attorney tested positive, and the next day Governor Cuomo tweeted that there were 22 confirmed cases. The governor tweeted another update on March 6, announcing that NY then had a total of 44 cases, promising to, "...continue providing updates to the public." Indeed, by this time the New York governor was giving daily briefings on CNN (Cable News Network). On March 7, with 34 new cases, Governor Cuomo declared a State of Emergency. A neighboring governor, Governor Phil Murphy, representing New Jersey, also declared a State of Emergency two days later. New Jersey had a total number of 11 cases at that stage. The first death from the virus in New Jersey was announced on March 10, a 69-year-old man who worked at a racetrack.

At a press conference on March 12, NYC mayor since 2014, Bill De Blasio, announced 42 more cases than the previous day, increasing the known number to 95. On March 13, Governor Cuomo announced during one of his daily news briefing updates that New York had 421 cases, which included more than 150 in the city. New Jersey had 69 cases by this time. For those who tuned in daily, or almost daily, to Governor Cuomo's aired updates, one could see a sharp rise as numbers climbed what he often referred to as "the mountain" of cases, but where would it end? Everyone knew that it would end, someday, as there was a finite number in the population, a very large population, most likely our nation's largest population. Eventually, regardless of the steepness of the climb, the numbers would slow, and then eventually cease, yet at what cost? How many lives where even one loss was too many?

I watched the various news channels, Cuomo's updates and White House Briefings as an interested citizen, and as a mental health practitioner to help me to address these issues to help my patients, also watching as a potential victim, interested in the "curve," curious as to whether the top would be a point, a plateau, or a seemingly never-ending rise with a miserably slow decline. Would the curve bounce up and down like a child's ball? Nobody knew. So, we watched. How fast could we learn? Would our actions be enough? Could we get ahead of the virus? I always felt that if it could be stopped in New York and the surrounding densely populated areas, then it could be stopped anywhere. So I watched, and meticulously kept records in the hope that if I did keep records, that they might be used in the future to answer vital questions: How was the last pandemic survived? What did they do? What worked and what did not? How was it for the average person trying to survive? What changed in daily life? This is an account intended not only for individuals facing such an event in the future, as history proves that it will happen again, but this is also an account of what we learned. There is an old saying, often quoted in several different variations, but it is thought to most likely originate from the writer and philosopher George Santayana, "Those who cannot learn from the past are condemned to repeat it."

By the end of the day on March 17, New York had more than 1,600 cases in the state, nearly half in the city, and 15 deaths. These numbers rose dramatically following a record number of tests being performed on March 19, increasing the number of positive cases to 5,638, and 36 deaths. Within three days, New York had 15,168 cases, with New Jersey's numbers intensifying to 1,914 cases. On March 24, Governor Murphy, representing the state with the second largest number of cases, informed the public that the caseload for his state had escalated to 3,675. On this same day, it was announced that New York intended to commence experimental clinical trials. New York would be the first state to treat the critically ill through the use of antibodies taken from the plasma of those who had recovered from the virus. Physicians would also use the malaria drug, Hydroxychloroquine, combined in treatment with the antibiotic Zithromax.

Americans were starving for good news. Each day seemed to begin with a new emotional beating as the numbers of those dying seemed to soar at a near-equal pace that the economy plunged. In a similar manner as the Diamond Princess, it was my opinion that New York was America's petri dish as other states across the nation had growing numbers at what seemed to be much slower rates. Other states also had slightly more time to prepare, to watch those states where the virus was already wreaking havoc, watching how the more populated states were responding, what was working, and what was not.

The numbers rose quickly to the point where Governor Andrew Cuomo issued an executive order to close down all non-essential businesses, leaving the public transportation system open. Once again, how to address this viral attack was something that was changing almost daily as new issues arose, some which were expected, other issues which may not have been so readily anticipated. Although some questioned leaving the public transportation system open, it is undeniable that this system is a key to New York City's economy for people to travel to work, for essential workers to get to work. Nevertheless, the subway had another problem as it was often used as a shelter by the homeless, with a recognizable challenge to contain the virus in the largest public transportation system in North America, serving millions.

New York's largest convention hall, the Jacob K. Javits Center, located on Manhattan's Westside corridor, was converted at this time into a 1,000-bed emergency hospital. Opening on April 3, 1986, this 1.8 million square foot center that had intended to host the 2020 World Floral Expo at this time, had been transformed to handle the overflow of patients due to the pandemic. Refrigerator trucks were also set up outside several hospitals in anticipation of there being an overflow of bodies, as was seen during the previous weeks in Italy.

March 25 saw the first glimmer of hope with news that the rate of increase in COVID-19 hospitalizations in New York was easing. Sadly, the rate of deaths kept rising. Schools remained closed as the community continued to stay-at-home and practice social distancing.

By March 27, New York had over 23,000 cases and 365 deaths. It was said that the Queens area was the most affected, accounting for roughly 34 percent of the deaths.

The USNS Comfort docked in New York City on March 30. Like her sister ship, USNS Mercy, Comfort was built as an oil tanker in 1976 by the National Steel and Shipbuilding Company, serving with the US Navy since 1987, with her home port in Norfolk, Virginia since March of 2013. Her accolades are many, which includes being positioned near Kuwait during Operation Desert Storm in the Persian Gulf War from 1990 to1991, operating as a floating trauma center in support of Operation Iraqi Freedom in the Iraq War from 2002 to 2003, assisting with Hurricane Katrina in 2005, and more recently, 2017, helping with sick patients after the tragedy of Hurricane Maria. Having served long as a symbol of hope and healing for America, the Comfort arrived to assist with ongoing medical needs with her 1,000-bed total capacity, complete with 12 operating rooms.

By this time, daily life resembled a roller coaster. The number of deaths climbed up as the economy went down, hopes lifted, and then they were shattered with new tragedies, new numbers, more death, some new spark in the haystack to extinguish. The arrival of the Comfort lifted hopes, and then the next day arrived with the announcement that the number of cases in New York had risen to 43,139, closing out the end of March 2020 with the number of deaths in NYC surpassing 1,000. This included the first COVID-19 death of a child being recorded on March 31.

Nobody was laughing in New York on April Fool's Day, April 1. Numbers had risen to 83,712 positive cases and nearly 2,000 deaths. News footage showed social distancing difficulties with playgrounds and similar, so playgrounds were closed. Connecticut was also reporting a new surge in cases. By the next day, New York had surpassed China, still presumed as the source of the outbreak, with New York reporting 92,381 cases. Of course, many were still questioning the numbers coming out of China.

By April 5 there were 122,031 cases and 4,159 deaths noted in New York. This day is also of note for a four-year-old Bronx Zoo Malayan tiger, named Nadia, being diagnosed with COVID-19, which represented the first known case of an animal being diagnosed with the virus. Indeed, it was later found that several of the other cats had the virus. Their infections seemed to have been contracted from an infected worker at the zoo, representing also the first known case of an animal being infected with the virus from human contact.

Good news came on April 7 as it was revealed that the total number of hospitalizations in New York was entering a plateau. ICU admissions and intubations were decreasing. Finally! Sadly, the number of deaths was still increasing. The hopes go up, only to go back down. Nevertheless, the curve was indeed flattening.

An Associated Press article by Mike Stobbe on April 8, titled: Some Doctors Moving Away From Ventilators for Virus Patients, reported that:

As health officials around the world push to get more ventilators to treat coronavirus patients, some doctors are moving away from using the breathing machines when they can. The reason: Some hospitals have reported unusually high death rates for coronavirus patients on ventilators, and some doctors worry that the machines could be harming certain patients.

He later explained that:

Mechanical ventilators push oxygen into patients whose lungs are failing. Using the machines involves sedating a patient and sticking a tube into the throat. Deaths in such sick patients are common, no matter the reason they need the breathing help. Generally speaking, 40% to 50% of patients with severe respiratory distress die while on ventilators, experts say. But 80% or more of coronavirus patients placed on the machines in New York City have died, state and city officials say.

Stobbe quoted Dr. Albert Rizzo, the American Lung Association's chief medical officer, as stating, "Higher-than-normal death rates also have been reported elsewhere in the US." He further clarified, "Similar reports have emerged from China and the United Kingdom. One UK report put the figure at 66%. A very small study in Wuhan, the Chinese city where the disease first emerged, said 86% died." He later added that:

"...Some health professionals have wondered whether ventilators might actually make matters worse in certain patients, perhaps by igniting or worsening a harmful immune system reaction...experts do say ventilators can be damaging to a patient over time, as high-pressure oxygen is forced into the tiny air sacs in a patient's lungs...some doctors say they're trying to keep patients off ventilators as long

as possible, and turning to other techniques instead...But increasingly, physicians are trying other measures first. One is having patients lie in different positions — including on their stomachs — to allow different parts of the lung to aerate better. Another is giving patients more oxygen through nose tubes or other devices. Some doctors are experimenting with adding nitric oxide to the mix, to help improve blood flow and oxygen to the least damaged parts of the lungs.

By April 10, New York had 170,512 cases, with 7,844 deaths. New Jersey reported 54,588 cases and 1,932 deaths. Connecticut, also in the tri-state, had 10,538 cases and 448 deaths.

By the time Easter Sunday arrived, April 12, the numbers were as follows:

New York: 1,888,694 cases, 9,385 deaths

New Jersey: 61,850 cases, 2,350 deaths

Connecticut: 12,035 cases, 554 deaths

Sadly, there was no multi-denominational service for the whole nation, or world, to watch and share.

On April 13, it was announced that the governors of New York, New Jersey, Connecticut, Delaware, Rhode Island, and Pennsylvania would be working together to coordinate a reopening of their states. Massachusetts joined to make a seventh member. This was part of the consortium the governor of New York, Andrew Cuomo, had previously mentioned. Other states across the country were also beginning to form consortiums as the country began to think about reopening the country, and the economy.

It is worth noting that, despite flattening the curve, the rise in the number of cases and deaths still continued, just as they continued to rise across the country. However, New York had proven that what was often referred to as "the beast" could be controlled...but at great cost. Meanwhile, patients, friends, neighbors, and family were breathing a sigh of relief with this small flicker of hope, while many continued to claim that, "I hear it might come back again in the fall." Always trying to maintain perspective, I would repeatedly caution that the virus had never left; it was not conquered; our unwanted visitor was still lurking in the shadows, and growing.

PERSPECTIVE

April 15: (WORLD)

Total world cases: 2,015,571 (increase of 24,588 from the day beforehand)

Deaths: 127,635 (increase of 1,701 from the day beforehand)

Recovered: 491,911(increase of 24,914 from the day beforehand)

Active Cases: 1,396,025; Mild: 1,344,508 (96 %), Critical: 51,517 (4%),

Closed: 619,546

Italy: 162,488

China: 82,295, New: 46, Deaths: 3,341

UK: not updated

Italy: not updated

April 15: (USA)

Total cases: 614,246 (an increase of 3,779 from the day beforehand)

Deaths: 26,064

Recovered: 38,820

Active Cases: 549,362, Critical: 13,473

Massachusetts: 28,163

New cases: 957

Cape Cod: 514, (possibly not updated)

Texas: 14,624, Deaths 957

New York: 213,779, Deaths: 11,586

Connecticut: The state reported that numbers increased substantially on April 15, with a new death toll of 868 and confirmed cases jumping to 14,755. The governor of Connecticut, Ned Lamont, explained that some of these numbers were individuals who had died in their homes and had therefore not previously been counted, with officials also clarifying that the new high figures might also be attributed to delays in reporting. Also on April 15, New Jersey reported a total of 71,030 cases, with 3,156 deaths.

The Dow Jones closed at 23,504.35 on April 15, 2020.

The FTSE closed at 5,597.65 on April 15, 2020.

On April 16, California announced that it intended to make undocumented immigrants eligible for cash payments from a $125 million coronavirus disaster relief fund. According to a CNN release by Madeline Holcombe and Catherine Shoichet, it was announced that the benefit would provide $500 of support for each adult, with a cap of $1,000 for each household. According to their CNN release, California Governor Gavin Newson stated that, "We feel a deep sense of gratitude for people that are in fear of deportation but are still addressing the essential needs of tens of millions of Californians."

The day closed with my son calling to let me know that he and his wife had just returned from Children's Hospital in Boston with their son, my grandson, Nathan. He had not wanted to alarm me earlier, so they had therefore chosen not to call at 3 AM that morning when their pediatrician instructed them to take Nathan to the ER due to having a very bad rash, high fever, and rectal bleeding. My son, Mark, stated that several tests had been performed and medication given, and that, "Nathan's fine. We just didn't want to worry you until we knew what was happening."

Next time...worry me please.

PERSPECTIVE

It was also around this time that I was hearing of suicides and suicide attempts due to fears instilled by COVID-19, fears of death, fears of lost pensions and a sense of either dying from the virus, or surviving and having no means of surviving after the virus was gone. As practitioners, we are always watchful for suicidal and homicidal ideation. We try hard to protect our patients and to promote their mental health, and I feared the impact of the media frenzy on my patients and others around me. The Health Insurance Portability and Accountability Act (HIPAA) was adopted in 1996 to regulate the flow of healthcare details and information, rightly protecting the information of patients, so I cannot speak as to patients, only noting that this month ended with references to suicide, suicidal ideation, and general unrest echoing far too often in the media. It was alarming. I feared for my patients, my friends, my family, the community, and even for myself. All still seemed to be safe, but where was this heading? I had a strong and horrifying sense that the virus was not the only thing fueling the rising tensions.

"Suicide doesn't end the chances of life getting worse, it eliminates the possibility of it ever getting any better."

– Unknown

CHAPTER 12
The Other Side of the Mountain

Social distancing and the stay-at-home orders were slowly, all too slowly, beginning to work as many states extended their stay-at-home orders. The number of hospitalizations were also slowing in many states, yet still rising in some areas, generally where the spread of the virus had arrived later. Several states were also issuing orders to wear masks with the hope that this added feature would further restrict another surge.

The curve was flattening, but we were by no means safe from the virus. We had learned how to control COVID-19, but we were still in danger, and not just from the virus. Our economy and entire way of life was threatened. Many saw their pensions and life-savings evaporating as the numbers of those unemployed continued to rise. Protests began to erupt across America to lift the stay-at-home orders. One of the first protests occurred when thousands of vehicles descended on Michigan's capital in Lansing on April 15, reporting an attendance of over 3,000 protesters in a reaction titled "Operation Gridlock," with vehicles clogging the streets surrounding the capitol building and a reported nearly 200 protesting on the capitol lawns. Michigan's protest lasted over eight hours and would soon be followed by another protest at the end of the month with similar outbreaks flaring up in Oklahoma, Kentucky, Rhode Island, and North Carolina, where protesters demanded a re-opening and easing of restrictions. Over the next two weeks, over half the states had witnessed demonstrations, along with similar protests in Belgium, India, Poland, Iraq, the Ivory Coast, and the UK.

An announcement was made by US Vice President Mike Pence on April 17, informing the public that America had enough tests to commence Phase One of reopening the country. On the same day, Governor Cuomo tweeted:

I'm issuing an Executive Order directing all public and private labs in NY to coordinate with the State Department of Health to ensure prioritizing diagnostic testing for public health and restarting the economy.

Although the virus had mercifully slowed, events did not. We were essentially ahead of the contagion, yet headline-worthy news continued to arrive in our emotional laps almost daily. April 20 was no different, but the best part was that it was more good news, and we were thirsty for anything good to hear. On this day, New York reported its lowest single-day death figure than it had in several weeks. On this same day, Israeli Haaretz News reported not only a drop in the number of patients on ventilators, but also that Israel had reached the stage of having more recoveries than new cases. Meanwhile, some hospitals and clinics began to resume elective surgeries and non-emergency treatments; President Trump temporarily suspended immigration to the United States for 60 days, and the first "Digital Immunity Cards," were issued in Chili to those who had recovered from COVID-19. The intention was to identify those who no longer posed a health risk -- which was a growing number.

April 20: (WORLD)
Total world cases: 2,498,999 (increase of 135,901 from the day beforehand)
Deaths: 171,334 (increase of 9,239 from the day beforehand)
Recovered: 657,895 (increase of 50,278 from the day beforehand)
Active Cases:1,669,770, Mild: 1,612,132 (97%), Critical: 829,229 (3%), Closed: 619,546
Italy: 181,228
China: 82,758, New: 11, Deaths: not updated
UK: 124,743, Deaths: 16,509, Active cases: 107,890, Total cases/1 Mil pop: 243

April 20: (Diamond Princess)
Total cases: 712
Total deaths: 13
Active cases: 55
Recovered: 644
Critical cases: 7

<u>April 20: (USA)</u>
Total cases: 792,938 (an increase of 51,708 from the day beforehand)
Total cases/1 Mil population: 2,396
Total deaths/1Mil population: 128
Deaths: 42,518
Recovered: 72,389
Active Cases: 678,031, Critical: 13,951
Massachusetts: 39,643, New cases: 1,566, Deaths: 1,809
Cape Cod: 664
Texas: 19,970
New York: 247,152, Deaths: 14,347
Connecticut: 19,815, Deaths: 1,331

The Dow Jones closed at 23,650.44 on April 20, 2020.
The FTSE closed at 5,812.83 on April 20, 2020.

"Change does not roll in on the wheels of inevitability, but comes through continuous struggle. And so we must straighten our backs and work for our freedom. A man can't ride you unless your back is bent."

– Martin Luther King

CHAPTER 13
So When Did the Virus Come to America?

An article appeared on April 21 titled: 2 Californians Died of Coronavirus Weeks Before Previously Known 1st US Case. Written by Jason Hanna, Sarah Moon and Stella Chan at CNN, they revealed that, "New autopsy results show two Californians died of novel coronavirus in early and mid-February —– up to three weeks before the previously known first US death from the virus." They postulated that:

These deaths now stand as the country's earliest two attributed to the coronavirus, a development that appears to shift the understanding of how early the virus was spreading in the country, health experts told CNN Wednesday.

Later in their article, they clarify that, "The two in California had no "significant travel history" that would have exposed them to the virus, Dr. Sara Cody, the county's chief medical officer, told reporters Wednesday in San Jose.

"We presume that each of them" caught the virus through community spread," she said."(This) tells us we had community transfer far earlier than we had known, and that indicates the virus was probably introduced and circulating far earlier than we had known," Cody said.

The next day, it was announced that Michael Bloomberg, a former mayor of New Your City, and just weeks earlier a Democratic presidential candidate, was committing roughly $10 million towards contact tracing. At the same time, the White House administration struck a deal with Congress for more coronavirus relief in a $484 billion bill that would provide fresh aid to small businesses and hospitals. President Trump said on Twitter that he supported the legislation.

Germany approved its first trials for a vaccine on April 22, on the same day that it was announced that Hydroxychloroquine was first found to be an ineffective treatment for the virus that had killed so many. Nevertheless, it was also announced that there were close to a hundred trials being explored, offering hope for a solution, and/or an effective treatment.

Cheryl Powell

As with almost everything related to this virus, new information was always emerging as we learned more and more about this invisible assailant, what President Trump still often referred to as the "Invisible Enemy" where, as in wartime one needs to assess the enemy, find the weak spots, strategize ways to win the war. We had already seen figures suggesting that men were more susceptible than women, and there were also suggestions that those with blood type A were more vulnerable. By the middle of April, new figures were emerging regarding race. On April 22, the CDC put out a release titled: "COVID-19 in Racial and Ethnic Minority Groups | CDCv.2019-ncov, racial-ethnic-minorities." It stated that:

The effects of COVID-19 on the health of racial and ethnic minority groups is still emerging; however, current data suggest a disproportionate burden of illness and death among racial and ethnic minority groups. A recent CDC MMWR report included race and ethnicity data from 580 patients hospitalized with lab-confirmed COVID-19 found that 45% of individuals for whom race or ethnicity data was available were white, compared to 55% of individuals in the surrounding community. However, 33% of hospitalized patients were black compared to 18% in the community and 8% were Hispanic, compared to 14% in the community. These data suggest an overrepresentation of blacks among hospitalized patients.

The release later commented on living conditions, stating that:

Members of racial and ethnic minorities may be more likely to live in densely populated areas because of institutional racism in the form of residential housing segregation. People living in densely populated areas may find it more difficult to practice prevention measures such as social distancing. Research also suggests that racial residential segregation is a fundamental cause of health disparities. For example, racial residential segregation is linked with a variety of adverse health outcomes and underlying health conditions. These underlying conditions can also increase the likelihood of severe illness from COVID-19. Many members of racial and ethnic minorities live in neighborhoods that are further from grocery stores and medical facilities, making it more difficult to receive care if sick and stock up on supplies that would allow them to stay home. Multi-generational households, which may be more common among some racial and ethnic minority families, may find it difficult to take precautions to protect older family members or isolate those who are sick, if

110

space in the household is limited," clarifying also that racial and ethnic minority groups are over-represented in jails, prisons and detention centers.

The CDC release also commented on work circumstances, claiming that these populations were more likely to be workers in essential industries, where, "Nearly a quarter of employed Hispanic and Black or African American workers are employed in service industry jobs compared to 16% of non-Hispanic whites," and that:

Hispanic workers account for 17% of total employment, but constitute 53% of agricultural workers; Black or African Americans make up 12% of all employed workers, but account for 30% of licensed practical and licensed vocational nurses.

Although everyone seemed to be progressively more disillusioned with the onslaught against the President, and also bearing in mind my platform of being fair and non-partisan, I cannot deny being surprised when, on April 23, President Trump erroneously made a suggestion during one of his White House briefings, that I knew immediately upon hearing him would top the headlines of the next day, sending me back to check the footage to verify the resulting accusations. In reality, his comments, and resulting comments, seemed to be taken out of context. More than any other president in my lifetime, President Trump addressed and updated his citizens regularly. This, in my opinion, made him contradictorily both more, and less, vulnerable. He made a point of stating facts as he knew them to ensure that they could not be altered by media reports, which simultaneously made him more vulnerable for errors.

On April 23, he initially spoke of his administration continuing to:

...leverage the Defense Production Act to dramatically increase the manufacture and delivery of critical medical supplies. We finalized three contracts to produce 39 million more N95 masks in 90 days.

He continued to comment on how:

Convalescent plasma will also be used to manufacture a concentrated antibody treatment that does not have to be matched with a particular blood type. This concentrated antibody treatment could be used as a preventative measure to keep healthcare workers and other high-risk populations from contracting the virus in the first place.

He informed the public that the Vice President was providing each state governor with a breakdown of the distributed personal protection, proceeding with comments on how:

[The] FDA has recently begun a national effort to expand access to convalescent plasma donated from the blood of those who have recovered from the virus. The blood of these donors contains antibodies that can potentially reduce the severity of the illness in those who are sick...

He clarified that, "Nearly 3,000 patients are now enrolled in the Expanded Access Program, receiving transfusions nationwide."

It was reported that 35,000 National Guard had been deployed across the country and that an excess of 4,500 active duty military doctors, nurses, and medical assistants had been deployed.

The briefing continued with the effects of solar light and humidity on the virus, and the impact on the half-life of COVID-19 in relation to aerosol testing.

President Trump responded, almost eagerly, and what appeared, at least to me as a mere citizen, to be responding out of excitement due to the hopeful news, stating that, "I see the disinfectant that knocks it out in a minute, one minute," continuing with what seemed to be more of an exploration than a suggestion:

And is there a way we can do something like that by injection inside, or almost a cleaning? Because you see it gets inside the lungs and it does a tremendous number on the lungs, so it would be interesting to check that.

I knew he was in trouble for this, and I confess that I felt sorry for the President. It was obvious that he was trying very hard to address what was a near-impossible situation, desperate to find a solution to cure the nation.

The question posed by the President was expectedly, and understandably, met by the manufacturer of Lysol responding with a warning against injecting or otherwise ingesting disinfectants. He had posed a question, obviously thinking on his feet, urging exploration, yet I soon started hearing accusations about his advising the public to ingest or inject disinfectants, when that did not seem to be true...but this was an election year.

Meanwhile, I was continuing to work, trying desperately to keep my patients calm and focused. I stressed perspective time and again. I tried to be reassuring, trying to counter their fears with perspective while attempting to simultaneously maintain my own sanity, my own perspective, offering what hope was possible without lying or being disingenuous. I had left the office several weeks earlier to work from home. Whenever possible, I tried to use FaceTime, Skype, or Zoom. Oddly, the majority of my patients either did not have these options, or flat-out rejected the idea. Therapy had changed dramatically. Ninety percent of communication is non-verbal so, at first, I strongly urged them to comply with the request, as I was concerned about the healthcare system for which I worked being reimbursed by the insurance companies. We were working in a declared State of Emergency, and life would return to some-sort of "normal," but then the finances would need to be sorted, eventually. However, I soon abandoned my urgings, beyond a simple request for video telecommunication sessions after I came to realize that, just as I was now being more lax and wearing jeans – yet still with a proper shirt -patients might also become more lax. Nevertheless, video telecommunication worked well with most patients who had this facility, and especially with the children, who adored an opportunity to show me their dogs, cats, pet frogs, mice, and several goldfish. I will never be able to remember all the names. However, I became less zealous in pursuing those who declined the video option. What I also discovered was that I suddenly had less no-shows, and I suspect this was due to a combination of the patient not needing to make an effort to come into the office, combined with our new circumstances - the mutually-shared threat of COVID-19 that was menacing the entirety of the human race, with the exception of those with a diagnosis that provided them with a resulting happy place from the pandemic. Everyone is different.

The results of New York's antibody study were also released on April 23, which indicated that roughly 14 percent of the 3,000 random samples from 40 locations in 19 counties had tested positive. This translated that these individuals had unsuspectedly had the virus at some earlier stage and recovered. During his daily briefing, Governor Cuomo explained that this equated to 2.7 million infections in the state.

On April 24, the state of Georgia commenced reopening, beginning with gyms, hair salons, tattoo parlors, and massage therapists. The governor of Georgia also opened bowling alleys? The new normal...

By April 25, a good portion of the world's deaths were in America, this being revealed on the same day that the WHO reported that there was no evidence that those who have recovered from the virus have immunity from being infected a second time.

April 26: (WORLD)
Total world cases: 3,007,194
Deaths: 207,265
Recovered: 883,298
Active Cases: 1,916,631, Mild: 1,859,018 (97%), Critical: 57,613 (3%),
Closed: 1,090,563
Italy: 197,675
China: 82,830, New: 3, Deaths: 4,633
UK: 152,840, Deaths: 20,732, Active cases: 131,764, Critical: 1,559,
Deaths/1 mil pop: 305

April 26: (USA)
Total cases: 987,322
Total cases/1 Mil pop: 2,983
Total Deaths/1Mil pop: 167
Deaths: 55,415
Recovered: 118,781
Active Cases: 813,126, Critical: 15,143
Massachusetts: 53,348, Deaths: 2,730
Cape Cod: 772
Texas: 25,206
New York: 362,991, Deaths: 28,802
Connecticut: 25,269, ,Deaths: 1,925, on the plateau
Michigan: 37,751, Deaths: 3,314, on the plateau
Georgia: 22,459, Deaths: 907, on the plateau
California: 43,691, Deaths: 1,716, slight rise
Illinois: 43,903, Deaths: 1,943, slight rise
Wyoming: 371, Deaths: 7, slight rise

Oregon: 2,311, Deaths: 91, slight rise
Ohio: 15,963, Deaths: 728, other side of the mountain
Missouri: 6,997, Deaths: 282, on the plateau
Montana: 448, Deaths: 14, other side of the mountain
Hawaii: 599, Deaths: 14, other side of the mountain

It was on April 27 that Governor Cuomo spoke of his state's second set of antibody testing results, which indicated that almost 15 percent tested positive. The next day, the Thunderbirds and Blue Angels flew in honor formation over New York and Newark. The country was beginning to hope again, with trepidation, but the change was palpable.

The Dow Jones closed at 24,133.78 on April 27, 2020.
The FTSE closed at 5,846.79 on April 27, 2020.

Sadly, it was on this day that an announcement was made that a prominent 49-year-old New York Medical Director committed suicide at her home in Virginia. It was commented that she was a "...casualty of the war in the trenches..." With respect to the eminent doctor's family, I do not list the name, yet also note a release from *Brain, Behavior, and Immunity*, dated April 23, 2020, just four days earlier and titled: COVID 2019-Suicide: A global psychological pandemic, where the article lists seven other suicides, the youngest being only aged 19. It had started...

As of April 29, 185 countries were impacted, with 3,157,549 cases worldwide.

By the last day of the month, New York Governor Cuomo was announcing that the subways would be closing for four hours each night for cleaning, commencing May 6. I confess that I cringed on hearing this. It takes only one person, one non-symptomatic individual, and only one subway rider to spread the virus. I considered this proposal and found myself remembering a caution I would often use to challenge my children: to not criticize unless you can propose a better solution. I had none.

On April 30, NASCAR announced that it would resume its season, without fans.

"Where there is no struggle, there is no strength."

– Oprah Winfrey

CHAPTER 14
Cabin Fever

The month of May, May Day, commenced with another lockdown protest, this time in California's state capital, Sacramento. Once again, many protesters failed to wear masks. Social distancing was also compromised during another "gridlock," despite the organizer's website advising to stand six feet apart.

<u>May 1 (WORLD)</u>
Total Cases: 3,364,969
Deaths: 237,715
Recovered: 1,069,793
Active Cases: 2,057,461; Mild: 2,007,493 (98%), Critical: 49,968 (2%),
Closed: 1,307,508
Italy: 207,428, New cases: 1,965, Deaths: 28,236, Cases/1 mil pop: 3,431
China: 82,874, New: 12, Deaths: 4,633
UK: 177,454, Deaths: 27,510, Active cases: 149,600, Cases/1 mil
pop: 2,644, Deaths/1 Mil pop: 405
Spain: 242,988, New cases: 3,648, Deaths: 28,236, New deaths: 281

<u>May 1 (USA)</u>
Total cases: 1,112,259
Total cases/1 Mil pop: 3,360
Total Ddeaths/1Mil pop: 196
Total tests: 6,538,470
Deaths: 64,914
Recovered: 157,809
Active Cases: 889,536, Critical: 15,118
Massachusetts: 62,205, Deaths: 3,562
Cape Cod: 860
Texas: 28,087, Deaths: 782, Recovered: 13,353

California: 48,917, Deaths: 1,982
Louisiana: 28,001, Deaths: 1,862
Georgia: 26,237, Deaths: 1,131, on the plateau
Illinois: 52,918, Deaths: 2,355
Florida: 33,690, Deaths: 1,268

The Dow Jones closed at 24,465,16 on May 1, 2020.
The FTSE closed at 5,763.06 on May 1, 2020.

People were feeling isolated. Therapy was still constantly changing as everyone tried to adjust, including the therapists. We were told 2-weeks. Then it was two more weeks, then three. These changes existed not only in therapy, but spread to most other areas and interests, such as two town commissions where I have the pleasure to interact with and expand my interest with the community. Where we once had our meetings face-to-face with our attending community applicants in the Selectman's Conference Room at Town Hall, the Commissioners now also held meetings in a similar manner to telehealth via the internet – the new normal, which kept us isolated. It was the beginning of May, and I had personally been isolated for nearly eight weeks, venturing from my computer screen only a few times for supplies, and daily to let my dog, Mia, take me for my walk. As for my cat, a blue-eyed Birman named Missie, the only thing out of the ordinary was that she now needed to share the house during the day.

As previously stated, I felt that my patients were initially more resilient, which I attributed to their having already gathered an arsenal of techniques from which to draw upon for coping. However, the patterns between the former and the newer patients without previous therapy were still growing closer as several began to decompensate, with the common denominator being fear. Where therapy once centered on relationship issues, school or job matters, difficulties with either real or imaginary friends, fears of going outside and socializing, alcohol, drug, sex, or technology addictions, anger issues, mood swings, and dealing with grief, these had changed to focusing, now almost exclusively, on fears arising from the epidemic, then pandemic. Practically everyone, including friends, family, and colleagues, were saying the same thing: "We need to get this country running again." It seemed as if everyone had originally understood the need to flatten the curve and the initial stay-at-home orders were generally accepted, and respected, and everyone made preparations.

Nevertheless, one extension after another brought new stressors, fears from those not getting their dialysis, fears from those not receiving their chemotherapy or radiation treatment, fears from those with a wide array of other conditions who had their treatments repeatedly extended or placed on "temporary holds," fears from those losing their life savings and pensions, fears from those who worried if their jobs would still be there when the orders were finally lifted, a swiftly growing number of those who expressed fears of being used as a pawn for political purposes, and even fears from those who wanted the crisis to go on forever, expressing joy at receiving payments from the stimulus packages which amounted to more than they made before the pandemic, reportedly with some receiving the equivalent of a 35 percent pay increase due to the stimulus, and others who had happily come out of retirement to cash in. As for my patients who were initially almost enjoying applying their skills at the beginning of the isolation, some were now done with previous activities, with less enjoyment taking sessions to the beaches, picnic areas, woods or similar. Stress seemed to be on the rise in almost everyone I encountered and I hoped this would change after the isolation ended.

Perhaps more worrisome was that I noticed more people getting sick with non-COVID illnesses, both physically and emotionally, and with many reporting weight gains. As human beings, we build our immune systems through healthy living and interactions with our world. My personal fear was that our ongoing isolation from our usual environment might decrease our usual immunities, rendering us more vulnerable to infection, and ultimately more susceptible to the virus.

A 2004 study by E. M. Reiche, S.O. Nunes, and H. K. Morimoto on: Stress, Depression, the Immune System, and Cancer found that:

The links between the psychological and physiological features of cancer risk and progression have been studied through psychoneuroimmunology. The persistent activation of the hypothalamic-pituitary-adrenal (HPA) axis in the chronic stress response and in depression probably impairs the immune response and contributes to the development and progression of some types of cancer. Here, we overview the evidence that various cellular and molecular immunological factors are compromised in chronic stress and depression and discuss the clinical implications of these factors in the initiation and progression of cancer. The consecutive stages of the multistep immune reactions are either inhibited or enhanced as a result of previous or parallel stress experiences, depending on the type and intensity of the stressor and on the animal species, strain, sex, or age. In general, both stressors and depression are associated with the decreased cytotoxic T-cell and natural-killer-cell activities that affect processes such as immune surveillance of tumors, and with the events that modulate development and accumulation of somatic mutations and genomic instability.

An article by Kimberly Smith from The Conversation, dated March 16, 2020 and titled: Social Isolation Is Linked to Higher Levels of Inflammation, Studies Show, argued:

Being lonely or socially isolated can negatively affect your wellbeing. There is even research showing that it increases the risk of illnesses such as cardiovascular disease, dementia and depression. Some researchers suggest that loneliness and social isolation lead to poorer health because they increase inflammation. Inflammation is when your body tells your immune system to produce chemicals to fight off infection or injury. It can also occur when you experience psychological or social stress.

She continued her argument with:

Short-term, local inflammation – such as when you accidentally cut your finger – can be helpful, but having slightly elevated long-term inflammation is associated with poor health. Researchers propose that loneliness and social isolation are linked to this elevated long-term inflammation...we wanted to see if loneliness (the subjective state of feeling alone) and social isolation (the objective state of being alone) are linked to long-term inflammation...

She added, "To do this, we searched for all published studies that looked at loneliness with inflammation or social isolation with inflammation..." This study concluded:

...people who are more socially isolated have higher levels of two inflammatory chemicals: C-reactive protein and fibrinogen...Fibrinogen increases blood clotting and is higher when people have an injury or trauma. When

people have long-term increased levels of these inflammatory markers, it can lead to an increased risk of poorer health over time.

Another study by the Texas Medical Center dated November 2, 2019, by Shanley Pierce, titled: Isolation Can Affect the Overall Health of Seniors. found:

By nature, humans are a social species. Evolution has hardwired us to depend on our connections and interactions with others to survive and thrive. As people live longer, though, they tend to have smaller social networks, due to retirement, declining health, mobility limitations and other challenges.

Pierce added that, "About 10,000 baby boomers turn 65 in the United States every day; by 2030, 20 percent of the American population will be 65 or older."

There are several studies that link social isolation and loneliness to a greater risk of health issues such as obesity, cardiovascular disease, high blood pressure, cancer, and weakened immune systems, along with an increased risk of developing depression and anxiety.

According to a CDC release dated April 27, 2020, titled: Loneliness and Social Isolation Linked to Serious Health Conditions, the CDC reported that, "Social isolation significantly increased a person's risk of premature death from all causes, a risk that may rival those of smoking, obesity, and physical inactivity," stating also, and referencing the *National Academies of Sciences, Engineering and Medicine, 2020*, that:

Social isolation was associated with about a 50% percent increased risk of dementia, that poor social relationships (characterized by social isolation or loneliness) was associated with a 29% increased risk of heart disease and a 32% increased risk of stroke, that loneliness was associated with higher rates of depression, anxiety, and suicide, and that loneliness among heart failure patients was associated with a nearly 4 times increased risk of death, 68% increased risk of hospitalization, and 57% increased risk of emergency department visits.

I was certainly witnessing the impact of extended isolation. It was palpable. It was shared. It was growing and I could not help but wonder which would take more causalities when all the numbers were finally tallied. Would it be the virus? Or would it be the cure?

"Never, never, never give up."

– *Winston Churchill*

CHAPTER 15
Bumps on the Far Side
of the Mountain

The curve seemed to be progressively trending down, yet nursing homes continued to be ground zero in all states.

With May 4 came an article in *The New York Times*, written by Tim Arango and Thomas Fuller, titled: Why Liberal Californians Don't Want to Go Back to Normal, reporting that:

...Already, thousands of people have been let out of the state's jails and prisons, cash bail has been eliminated for most crimes, thousands of homeless people now have roofs over their heads, and children in rural and poor areas of the state are being sent tens of thousands of laptop computers for distance learning.

The next day, May 5, was my daughter's birthday, and I seriously questioned what her world would look like in the future.

<u>May 6: (WORLD)</u>
Total world cases: 3,759,705
Deaths: 259,609
Recovered: 1,259,667
Active Cases: 2,240,429, Mild: 2,191,370 (98%), Critical: 49,059 (2%),
Closed: 1,519,276
Italy: 213,013, Deaths: 29,319, Cases/1 mil pop: 3,523, Deaths/1 mil pop: 485
China: 82,883, New: 2, Deaths: 4,633 (same as May 1)
UK: 194,990, Deaths: 29,315, Active Cases: 165,219, Critical: 1,559, Cases/1 mil pop: 2,872, Deaths/1 mil pop: 433
Spain: 253,682, New cases: 3,121, New Deaths: 244

May 6: (USA)
Total cases: 1,240,809
Total cases/1 Mil pop: 3,749
Total Deaths/1Mil pop: 219, Total tests /1 mil pop: 23,453,
Total tests: 7,763,022
Deaths: 72,463
Recovered: 201,879
Active Cases: 966,467, Critical: 16,179
Massachusetts: 69,087, Deaths: 4,090
Cape Cod: not available
Texas: not available

The Dow Jones closed at 23,664.64 on May 6, 2020.
The FTSE closed at 5,853.76 on May 6, 2020.

On May 7, Neiman Marcus filed for bankruptcy. This was the same day that Brazil's Congress approved two stimulus bills that would provide financial help to states and municipalities, setting aside 700 billion Reais ($122 billion) for their economic recovery.

May 7 also witnessed the representatives of six faiths offering prayers in the White House Rose Garden during the 2020 National Day of Prayer. President Trump had issued a White House release the previous evening, declaring,

On this National Day of Prayer, Americans reaffirm that prayer guides and strengthens our Nation, and we express, with humility and gratitude, our firm reliance on the protection of divine Providence. As one Nation under God, we share a legacy of faith that sustains and inspires us and a heritage of religious liberty. Today, we join together and lift up our hearts, remembering the words of 1 John 5:14 that tell us when "we ask anything according to His will, He hears us."

The release later added that:

Today, as much as ever, our prayerful tradition continues as our Nation combats the coronavirus. During the past weeks and months, our heads have bowed at places outside of our typical houses of worship, whispering in silent solitude for God to renew our spirit and carry us through unforeseen and seemingly unbearable hardships. Even though we have been unable to gather together in fellowship

124

with our church families, we are still connected through prayer and the calming reassurance that God will lead us through life's many valleys. In the midst of these trying and unprecedented times, we are reminded that just as those before us turned to God in their darkest hours, so must we seek His wisdom, strength, and healing hand. We pray that He comforts those who have lost loved ones, heals those who are sick, strengthens those on the front lines, and reassures all Americans that through trust in Him, we can overcome all obstacles.

The President concluded with:

In 1988, the Congress, by Public Law 100-307, as amended, called on the President to issue each year a proclamation designating the first Thursday in May as a National Day of Prayer, "on which the people of the United States may turn to God in prayer and meditation at churches, in groups, and as individuals.

NOW, THEREFORE, I, DONALD J. TRUMP, President of the United States of America, do hereby proclaim May 7, 2020, as a National Day of Prayer. I encourage all Americans to observe this day, reflecting on the blessings our Nation has received and the importance of prayer, with appropriate programs, ceremonies, and activities in their houses of worship, communities, and places of work, schools, and homes consistent with the White House's "Guidelines for Opening up America Again.

IN WITNESS WHEREOF, I have here unto set my hand this sixth day of May, in the year of our Lord two thousand twenty, and of the Independence of the United States of America the two hundred and forty-fourth.

The next day, the Rose Garden and those gathered at the White House saw the President addressing those gathered, stating that, "In recent weeks and days, our country has endured a grave hardship." He continued, "I ask all Americans to join their voices and their hearts in spiritual union as we ask our Lord in heaven for strength and solace, for courage and comfort, for hope and healing, for recovery and for renewal."

Six ministers of faith spoke at this 2020 National Day of Prayer, with representatives from the Latter-Day Saints, Evangelicals, Catholics, Muslims, Jews, and Hindus, these being represented by Sister Anida Martinez, a Catholic nun, Pujari Harish Brahmbhatt spoke the Shanti, the Hindu prayer for peace; Rabbi Ariel Sadwin addressed the nation from the Rose Garden, as did Bishop

Dwight Green of the Pentecostal Church of God in Christ, US Army Islamic Chaplain Lt. Col. Ibraheem Raheem, Sister Debbie Harrison, Pastor Paula White, and Pastor Brittney Atkinsola. All were followed by the Spirit of Faith Christian Center Choir singing "God Bless America."

Did the President receive my e-mail? Whether he did or he did not – Halleluiah!

May 7: (WORLD)
Total world cases: 3,836,819
Deaths: 265,366
Recovered: 1,308,201
Active cases: 2,263,252, Mild: 2,215,179 (98%), Critical: 48,073 (2%),
Closed: 1,573,567
Italy: 214,457, Deaths: 29,684, Deaths/1 mil pop: 491
China: 82,885, New: 2, Deaths: 4,633 (same as day beforehand)
UK: 201,101, Deaths: 30,076, Active Cases: 170,681, Cases/1 mil pop: 2,962, Deaths/1 mil pop: 443.

May 7: (USA)
Total cases: 1,263,243
Total cases/1 Mil pop: 3,816, Total Deaths/1Mil pop: 226
Total tests/1 mil pop: 24,186, Total tests: 8,005,589
Deaths: 74,809
Recovered: 213,109
Active Cases: 975,325, Critical: 15,827
Massachusetts: 72,025, Deaths: 4,420
Cape Cod: 997, Deaths: 55
Texas: 32,332, Deaths: 884
New York: 319,000, Deaths: 19,415
California: 54,937, Deaths: 2,254
Louisiana: 29,673, Deaths: 1,991 (still going down the mountain)
Illinois: 63,840, Deaths: 2,662 (still going down the mountain)
Washington State: 15,462, Deaths: 841 (slightly up)

Michigan: 43,950, Deaths: 4,135
Pennsylvania: 50,092, Deaths, 2,458 (still going down the mountain)

The Dow Jones closed at 23,875.89 on May 7, 2020.
The FTSE closed at 5,935.98 on May 7, 2020.

May 8 saw the FDA authorizing the company Moderna to conduct Phase II of its proposed COVID-19 vaccine. Also on May 8, it was announced that the unemployment rate in America had risen the previous month to 14.7 percent, representing the highest post the Great Depression.

Another item of grim news haunted the American public on May 8 after it was announced that there were 73 cases of children presenting with a new pediatric multi-system inflammatory syndrome that was thought to be associated with the COVID-19 virus. Even worse, two children had died.

Until this point, one of the few blessings about the pandemic was that children were thought to be relatively immune to it, yet this new affliction, with symptoms that presented differently, sent the medical professionals scrambling back to check their records for previously treated children and teens.

At the time of writing this account, this news remains unclear. Like many aspects associated with the virus, the professionals clambered for answers, usually only to be presented with more questions. In the beginning of this revelation, there were small clusters of critically ill children with unusual symptoms, with these clusters arising in the US and also in the UK, originally identified as Pediatric Multisystem Inflammatory Syndrome (PMIS). Then it was noticed that many of these cases presented in a similar manner to another illness named Kawasaki Disease.

Those with Kawasaki usually presented with a high fever of over 101 degrees that would last for roughly four or five days and usually in conjunction with redness in the eyes, tongue, and lips, many with a rash and/or swelling in the hands, feet, and neck, along with possible diarrhea and abdominal pain. A search for more information revealed that several of the children tested positive for COVID-19, while many of the others had the antibodies. I heard the news, thought of my grandson, and prayed.

The next day, May 9, it was announced that Dr. Anthony Fauci from the White House task force had been in contact with a White House staffer who had tested positive for the virus. He would begin a modified two-week quarantine. The same announcement was made regarding the CDC Director Dr. Robert Redfield and FDA Director Dr. Stephen Hahn.

On May 11, New York's Governor Cuomo announced that the "pause" for his state would end on May 15 when the order for a statewide shutdown expired. Governors across the country were making similar announcements. On this same day, as the numbers of new victims continued to drop across America and Europe, Wuhan announced its first new case since they had lifted their lockdown.

May 12 saw the commencement of a hearing before the Senate Health, Labor and Pensions Committee. Testifying, mostly remotely, were Dr. Anthony Fauci, Dr. Robert Redfield, ADM Brett Giroir, MD, and Dr. Stephen Hahn. Dr. Fauci cautioned that the consequences could be serious if the country opened too quickly or improperly. Although I believed there to be much respect and appreciation for those testifying, the general reactions I witnessed from the public, who had endured over three years of threatened impeachment of an American President, followed by months of the actual hearings, railroading almost immediately afterwards into a raging pandemic that involved a current lockdown resembling a house arrest, resulted in a groaning "Please Not Again" response from many citizens of all political persuasions in reaction to more hearings.

May 13: (WORLD)
Total world cases: 4,362,016
Deaths: 293,304
Recovered: 1,613,164
Active Cases: 2,455,548, Mild: 2,409,216 (98%), Critical: 46,332 (2%),
Closed: 1,906,468
Italy: 221,216, Deaths: 30,911, Cases/1 mil pop: 3,659
China: 82,926, New: 2, Deaths: 4,633 (unchanged)
UK: 226,463, Deaths: 32,692, Active Cases: 193,427, Cases/1 mil pop: 3,336, Deaths/1 mil pop: 482

Spain: 269,520, Deaths: 26,920, Recovered: 180,470, Active Cases: 62,130
Russia: 242,271, New Cases: 10,028

May 13: (Diamond Princess)
Total cases: 712
Total deaths: 13
Active cases: 48
Recovered: 651
Critical cases: 4

May 13: (USA)
Total cases: 1,408,636
Total cases/1 Mil pop: 4,256, Total Deaths/1Mil pop: 252
Deaths: 83,425
Recovered: 296,746
Active cases: 1,028,465, Critical: 16,473
Massachusetts: 79,332, Deaths: 5,141
Cape Cod: 1,093, Deaths: 73
Texas: 39,869, Deaths: 1,100
New York: 340,661, Deaths: 22,013
California: 72,988
Louisiana: 36,925, Deaths: 2,545
Illinois: 84,698, Deaths: 3,792
Michigan: 48,391, Deaths: 4,714
Pennsylvania: 58,698, Deaths, 3,943

The Dow Jones closed at 23,247.97 on May 13, 2020.
The FTSE closed at 5,904.05 on May 7, 2020.

By May 14, nearly 3 million more Americans had filed for unemployment, bringing the total in the two months since the pandemic began to roughly 36 million. In contrast, Reuters released more hope on this day, May 14, in an article by Julie Steenhuysen, titled: Oxford Coronavirus Vaccine Found Protective in Small Monkey Study, where Ms. Steenhuysen reported:

Cheryl Powell

British drugmaker AstraZeneca last month announced it had teamed up with researchers at the Oxford Vaccine Group and the Jenner Institute, which are developing the vaccine. According to the report, some of the monkeys given a single shot of the vaccine developed antibodies against the virus within 14 days, and all developed protective antibodies within 28 days, before being exposed to high doses of the virus. After exposure, the vaccine appeared to prevent damage to the lungs and kept the virus from making copies of itself there, but the virus was still actively replicating in the nose.

She later reported that 1,000 people had received the vaccine as of May 13. On May 15, J.C. Penny filed for Chapter 11 bankruptcy protection.

"Healing yourself is connected with healing others."

– Yoko Ono

"It's when we start working together that the real healing takes place."

– David Hume

CHAPTER 16
Vaccines and Treatments

As one would anticipate, researchers around the world were searching to find a cure and before long there were roughly 70 studies in progress. As of March 20, there were 44 known vaccines being researched and a further announcement was released by the WHO in mid-April that the number had raised to 70. Finally, something very much needed was taking a climb up that mountain – hope. Nevertheless, by the middle of April at least three were in clinical trials, which meant that these were being tested on human participants. Since this version is an initial account and vaccine research is still very early, I will mention only a few, with the intention of providing far more information in a subsequent account after more is known.

MODERNA'S Covid-19 vaccine candidate, mRNA-1273: At the time of writing this account Moderna's COVID-19 vaccine was in Phase I of their clinical trials.

AstraZeneca's CALQUENCE: This research was undertaken by the UK-based AstraZeneca company in conjunction with Oxford University's Jenner Institute investigating this drug that was reportedly already approved for the treatment of Leukemia.

Also in the UK, the University of Oxford is reportedly launching more research, named **PRINCIPLE**, to assess pre-existing drugs for the treatment of patients aged above 50 years with signs of Covid-19. This study is apparently intended to be conducted in the GP practices, the UK's equivalent to Primary Care Physicians (PCP).

Another UK-based vaccine developer company, **STABILITECH**, was also entering the race by this time to find a vaccine, recognized by the World Health Organization (WHO) as a vaccine developer.

Remaining in the UK, the University of Birmingham also launched a clinical trial to evaluate various drugs for potentially treating Covid-19.

More research was being undertaken by the French-based pharmaceutical company **SANOFI** in collaboration with GlaxoSmithKline.

CanSino Biological: This vaccine is being researched by China and with the Beijing Institute of Biotechnology, and is allegedly in Phase II at the time of this account.

ABX464 from the Parisian biotech company, named **ABIVAX**, is another possibility, which treats acute respiratory distress syndrome. This drug was allegedly first developed to treat the inflammation associated with ulcerative colitis.

Next there is the antiviral drug, called **FAVIPIRAVIR**, being researched by the Russian Direct Investment Fund (RDIF), collaborating with the **Chem-Rar** Group. Their initial results allegedly showed that 60 percent of the 40 patients treated with the drug tested negative for coronavirus following five days of treatment.

It would seem that **Glenmark Pharmaceuticals**, which is India-based, was also researching **FAVIPIRAVIR** by this time. Favipiravir is an anti-flu drug.

Many other existing drugs were also being researched at the time of this account to serve either as a vaccine or as a treatment. These include **REMDE-SIVIR**, where *The New England Journal of Medicine* posted on June 11, 2020, referencing a previous NEJM posting and also a Gilead release on April 10, 2020, claimed that 68 percent of 53 patients in the hospital with COVID-19 indicated improvement after taking the drug.

The use of other existing drugs were also being explored, such working on a vaccine based on the measles vaccine, and also studying the potential use of anti-malaria drugs such as **CHLOROQUINE** and **HYDROXYCHLOROQUINE**.

These represent only a small portion of vaccines being developed throughout the world at the time of this account. I also only mention these briefly, as I am not a qualified researcher, nor a medical doctor, and therefore should not comment on their efficacy, also because the research is ongoing and may well not be accurate at the time this account is read, with an intention, as previously stated, to provide far more in a future account after more is known about this ever-changing pandemic.

"There is no coming to consciousness without pain."

– Carl Jung

CHAPTER 17
Not the First, and it Won't be the Last

With all the discussion about Armageddon and plagues, and the "angel of death," I decided to look further into this. Some I knew while others I was less acquainted with, bringing me to the conclusion that this will definitely happen again. One only needs to look at the history, and learn from it.

In roughly 3000 B.C., a plague wiped out an entire village in China at a site now known as Hamin Mangha in Northeastern China. It is thought that the contagion spread quickly, so much that there was no time for burials. Another site from roughly the same time period is also found in Northeastern China, called Miaozigou, where inhabitants suffered the same outcome, which is suggestive of a widely spread epidemic.

Another epidemic arose at about 430 BC, lasting five years, which decimated the Athenian culture and people, with estimates suggesting a death toll in excess of 100,000 inhabitants. Thucydides, a Greek historian (460-400BC) wrote that even healthy individuals, "...were all of a sudden attacked by violent heats in the head, and redness and inflammation in the eyes, the inward parts, such as the throat or tongue, becoming bloody..." as was later translated by author Richard Crawley in his book (translated) on: The History of the Peloponnesian War.

Believed to be a strain of the Bubonic Plague, the Plague of Justinian nearly destroyed the Byzantine Empire from A.D. 541-542, estimated to have killed nearly ten percent of the world population. Then, 1346-1353 witnessed the Black Death, which swept across Asia to Europe. Many accounts suggest that this killed roughly half of Europe's population.

We all learned in school how the Aztec and Inca populations were ravaged throughout the sixteenth century by illnesses brought to the Americas by European explorers and tradesmen, where it is suggested that nearly 90 percent of the indigenous population perished from diseases such as Smallpox.

Cheryl Powell

Killing another estimated 100,000, which included about 15 percent of the city inhabitants, the Great Plague of London began in April of 1665. This was caused by the fleas of infected rodents. It ended in 1666, where another catastrophe hit London on September 2 of that year, where the Great Fire of London lasted four days, burning large sections of the city. Oddly, whenever I read accounts of this time in London's history, I find myself questioning if the burning may have shortened the end of the plague and helped to prevent a resurgence of the disease.

The Russian Plague occurred between 1770-1772 under the reign of Catherine II, also known as Catherine the Great, again with a loss of nearly 100,000.

The first recorded epidemic on American shores, outside of those inflicted on the Native American population with the arrival of settlers, was the Yellow Fever Epidemic of 1793, which was transmitted through mosquitoes, killing over 5,000 and ending with the arrival of the colder winter months that defeated the mosquitoes.

Nearly a hundred years later, in 1889, the world was struck with another flu pandemic. It is worth noting that the previous 100 years had seen the emergence of a new industrial age with increased transportation of many forms. In a similar manner as COVID-19, the disease spread throughout the globe within a few months, reportedly taking more than a million lives.

America found itself in another epidemic in 1916, Polio, which began wreaking havoc in New York City with 27,000 cases and roughly 6,000 deaths in the US alone. Sadly, the main victims seemed to be the children, returning sporadically until 1954 when Dr. Jonas Salk developed a vaccine that was introduced in 1955.

Then there was the Spanish Flu, arising in 1918 and spanning two years – a mere 100 years ago. It is estimated that it killed roughly one-fifth of the over 500 million individuals impacted by this disease.

The Asian Flu Pandemic of 1957-1958, claiming more than a million lives, began in China. It is believed that it was actually a blend of avian flu viruses. Like COVID-19, it spread at an accelerated rate, reaching Singapore in February of 1957, Hong Kong in April of 1957, and the coastal cities of America later in the same year. America lost 116,000 souls, with an estimated 1.1 million perishing worldwide.

134

PANDEMIC 2020

An article dated May 1, 2020 and found in the AIER, *American Institute for Economic Research* was titled: Woodstock Occurred in the Middle of a Pandemic. Written by Jeffrey A. Tucker, Editorial Director for the American Institute for Economic Research, the author claims that the 1969 Woodstock festival occurred in the middle of a pandemic, elaborating that it had arrived in the United States in 1968 and that, "It ultimately killed 100,000 people in the U.S., mostly over the age of 65, and one million worldwide." He goes on to clarify that:

[The] lifespan in the US in those days was 70 whereas it is 78 today. Population was 200 million as compared with 328 million today. It was also a healthier population with low obesity. If it would be possible to extrapolate the death data based on population and demographics, we might be looking at a quarter million deaths today from this virus. So in terms of lethality, it was as deadly and scary as COVID-19 if not more so, though we shall have to wait to see.

Jeffrey A. Tucker astutely clarifies:

Nothing was closed by force. Schools mostly stayed open. Businesses did too. You could go to the movies. You could go to bars and restaurants... In fact, people have no memory or awareness that the famous Woodstock concert of August 1969 – planned in January during the worse period of death – actually occurred during a deadly American flu pandemic that only peaked globally six months later.

He makes a special notation later, that:

...A reader pointed me to an academic article that says, "23 [states] faced school and college closures" but implies that this was due to absenteeism. This further underscores how aware people were at the time of the disease, clarifying that the, "Stock markets didn't crash because of the flu. Congress passed no legislation. The Federal Reserve did nothing. Not a single governor acted to enforce social distancing, curve flattening (even though hundreds of thousands of people were hospitalized), or banning of crowds. No mothers were arrested for taking their kids to other homes. No surfers were arrested. No daycares were shut even though there were more infant deaths with this virus than the one we are experiencing now. There were no suicides, no unemployment, no drug overdoses attributable to flu.

Cheryl Powell

I was alive during that time. I do remember Woodstock because I wanted to go, yet I was far too young. Still, I have no memory of the pandemic this author mentions.

Another virus is believed to originate from a chimpanzee virus in West Africa in the 1920s, which then transferred to humans, commencing in 1981 and is still spreading, called AIDS. It is estimated to have claimed over 35 million lives as there was originally no known remedy, until this year, 2020. Although a medication was developed in the 1990s to allow those impacted to have a relatively normal life span, it was recently announced that two individuals have now been cured of HIV/AIDS.

The Swine Flu of 2009-2010 is allegedly believed to be caused by influenza infections in pigs. It is believed that this originated in Mexico before spreading around the world to infect roughly 1.4 billion people, killing an estimated 284,000, affecting mostly children and young adults. The vaccine for the H1N1 virus that caused the Swine Flu is now said to be included in the annual flu vaccine.

The years 2014-2016 saw the West African Ebola epidemic, with a reported 28,600 cases and 11,325 deaths, starting in Guinea in December of 2013, spreading afterwards to Liberia and Sierra Leone, where the outbreak seemed mostly restricted to these three countries, with a limited spread to Senegal, Nigeria, the US, and Europe. Like COVID-19, there is, at least to date and according to information I could find, no currently known cure for Ebola.

The Zika Virus epidemic from 2015 to current day is predominantly found in South and Central America. It is believed to spread through mosquitoes, but it can also be sexually transmitted between humans. Flourishing in warm climates, the Zika attacks infants that are still in the womb, causing birth defects.

The CDC revealed in an Associated Press release by Mike Stobbe, dated September 26, 2018 that, "An estimated 80,000 Americans died of flu and its complications last winter – the diseases highest death toll in at least four decades." Their release clarifies that:

Last fall and winter, the U.S. went through one of the most severe flu seasons in recent memory. It was driven by a kind of flu that tends to put more people in the hospital and cause more deaths, particularly among young children and the elderly. The season peaked in early February. It was mostly over by the end of March, although some flu continued to circulate.

Another article by Lisa Lockerd Maragakis, M.D., M.P.H., from John Hopkins Health and titled: Coronavirus Disease 2019 vs. The Flu, states that:

Influenza (the flu) and COVID-19, the illness caused by the coronavirus that's led to the current pandemic, are both infectious respiratory illnesses. Although the symptoms of COVID-19 and the flu can look similar, the two illnesses are caused by different viruses.

Ms. Maragakis, Senior Director of Infection at Johns Hopkins, explained how, despite sharing many symptoms, means of transmissions and ways to prevent transmission, that COVID-19 is, "Caused by one virus, the novel 2019 coronavirus, now called severe acute respiratory syndrome coronavirus 2, or SARS-CoV-2," whereas the flu is, "Caused by any of several different types and strains of influenza viruses," adding that:

While both the flu and COVID-19 may be transmitted in similar ways, there is also a possible difference: COVID-19 might be spread through the airborne route, meaning that tiny droplets remaining in the air could cause disease in others even after the ill person is no longer near.

Another release from the WHO, dated March 11, 2019, is titled: WHO Launches New Global Influence Strategy, stating:

Influenza remains one of the world's greatest public health challenges. Every year across the globe, there are an estimated 1 billion cases, of which 3 to 5 million are severe cases, resulting in 290 000 to 650 000 influenza-related respiratory deaths. WHO recommends annual influenza vaccination as the most effective way to prevent influenza. Vaccination is especially important for people at higher risk of serious influenza complications and for health care workers.

That is why I intend to shave off some of any profits, if any, from this account. History has shown us, despite all of our technology, that we are still vulnerable, and such epidemics and pandemics will continue to impact either later in our own lives, or threaten our future generations. Writing this account, and sharing, is one of my ways to contribute.

"Hope is being able to see that there is light despite all of the darkness."
– Desmond Tutu

CHAPTER 18
So What Did Happen to All the Toilet Paper

As mentioned earlier, I like to give my patients homework, promising that it is never graded. It is simply intended to keep them on track and focused on goals. During the Time of COVID, homework was also intended to keep them distracted when they could not identify other projects such as gardening, walking, exercising, cooking new food recipes, with family engaging in family nights, movie or game nights. Some I have writing a journal of their Time of COVID to remind them how they endured this time – and also to have for their own future generations. For others, and usually in an attempt to instill levity, the homework was to answer our director's question: "What I don't understand is whatever happened to all the toilet paper." It turned out to be somewhat of a scavenger hunt, occupying the mind, and the imagination, not only for patients, but I extended it to friends and family. After all, we find ourselves all in this psychological arena together. I list some of the better answers that were submitted for inclusion in this account, and without violating HIPAA with identities, and altering enough so that the contributors cannot be identified.

1. Use it with chicken wire to make a 2020 COVID Christmas Tree and stuff the TP into the little holes in the wire.
2. My mom said we could use it to help the plants to retain the water around the bases of new plants.
3. I'd like to stuff it in my ears, so I can't hear my boyfriend yelling at me.
4. It might be used when I propose to my girlfriend, putting it under the engagement ring in the box so that we remember the engagement took place during the Time of COVID. It brought us together.
5. I could stuff it into my pillow case as pillow stuffing.
6. I use it to clean my shoes.
7. It's good for taking make-up off.
8. We're out of paper towels, so we used TP like a paper towel.

9. My puppy likes to grab it at one end and then race around the house with it.
10. I use it to exercise my soccer. Me and my big brother kick it back and forth, trying to keep it in the air. I think we saw that idea on TV.
11. I could take it hiking with me and use it like breadcrumbs to find my way back.
12. I'm so upset now without going out that I use at least a roll each day to dry my tears.
13. I'd like to stuff it into my wife's mouth to stop her nagging me.
14. Sometimes I just want to put it into my teenager's mouth to stop her talking back. So rude.
15. My mom places some Vicks onto some TP and puts it by my pillow at night to help me sleep.
16. I could use TP to write a very long poem about TP.
17. We could use it to stuff into the cracks along the edges of the doors and windows to keep the virus out.
18. I use it as a toy to tease my cat. It's better than the wind-up toy where the batteries don't work anymore, and Mom won't go out just to get me new batteries.
19. My dad uses it to check the oil in the car and the mower.
20. I couldn't try to do anything with spare TP because my older sister hoards it all for her make-up.

And my two favorites:

1. We could tear it into long tails and tie them the deck and the trees on a specific day so that they blow in the wind to mark the end of the stay-at-home orders.
2. I could wrap it around my head several times, so I can't see what's going on until this all goes away.

"If you're embarking around the world in a hot-air balloon, don't forget the toilet paper."

– Richard Branson

CHAPTER 19
The End of the Beginning

So today is May 17, and tomorrow is the day the stay-at-home orders should be lifted in the state of Massachusetts, where I live and write this account, which explains why Massachusetts numbers are regularly checked and compared with the remoter part of the state, Cape Cod. Last Friday, May 15, the governor of this state, Charles Baker, promised to announce plans for reopening tomorrow. It therefore seems appropriate to end this first part of the Pandemic 2020 account on this day, to get this out to the public, and to commence the second phase of this ongoing account to explore what is ahead of us.

Yesterday, I visited with my son, his wife, and my six-month-old grandson. I cried intermittently during the one-hour drive home. These were tears of happiness, thanking God for keeping them safe, keeping them healthy, allowing me an opportunity to hug and kiss my grandson, who responded by using my ear as an anchor to twist and turn in my arms in an attempt to not miss absorbing absolutely everything in his environment, pulling my hair in his newly acquired ability to grasp and pull. It was wonderful! It was normal. I had an antibody test three days beforehand after learning that I had been exposed before the stay-at-home orders to a patient who had been diagnosed with the virus before our session. My results were negative, which was surprising to me in view of the UK physician's diagnosis of SARS nearly two decades ago. I was told to expect a positive result due to the previous diagnosis, and also due to the time that had elapsed before I learned of the patient's diagnosis. Do the antibodies not remain or somehow fizzle out? Was the SARS diagnosis incorrect, or was the SARS virus so different from the new Corona that it would not show up on this test? Like many things encountered during this episode in our lives, answers only result in more questions.

I had remained at home for the two weeks before making my trip to the Boston area for my visit to ensure that I was well and not a threat. I therefore went for groceries on my return, only to discover that at least half of the staff, cashiers, baggers, and even the floor manager were wearing their masks either off or under their nose. One young man was wearing his mask totally under his chin like a prophetic bow tie, while another had it so low under his nose that his moustache hung out over the top. It seems clear, at least to me as a mere observer, that keeping the country shut down will never work and will only serve to plunge the country more into debt, hurting the economy as people grow increasingly more restless to return to work so that their livelihoods are not lost forever. There will always be those who refuse to comply with instructions intended to keep them safe, believing that the guidelines simply do not pertain to them, feeling challenged and affronted that they are encouraged to do something that they simply do not want to do, that it might hide their cool moustache, or a pretty face and, whilst I agree with and protect any person's right to choose for him or herself, I also do not believe that anyone has the right to place another at risk. Nevertheless, it also seems clear that this virus will not go away until it has either run its course, we have acquired herd immunity, or until a vaccine is found – all of which I am personally convinced will happen, but only time will tell.

RESET

<u>May 17: (WORLD)</u>
Total world cases: 4,801,517
Deaths: 316,659
Recovered: 1,858,090
Active Cases: 2,626,768, Mild: 2,581,951 (98%), Critical: 44,817 (2%),
Closed: 2,174,749
Italy: 225,435, Deaths: 31,908
China: 82,954, New: 7, Deaths: 4,634
UK: 243,695, Deaths: 34,636, Cases/1 mil pop: 3,592, Deaths/1 mil pop: 511
Spain: 277,719, Deaths: 27,650, Recovered: 195,945
Russia: 281,752, Recovered: 67,373, Deaths: 2,631

<u>May 17: (USA)</u>
Total Cases: 1,527,664

Total Cases/1 Mil pop: 4,619
Total Deaths/1Mil pop: 275,
Total Tests: 11,875,580, Total Tests/1 mil pop: 35,903
Deaths: 90,978
Recovered: 346,389
Active Cases: 1,090,297
Critical: 16,355
Massachusetts: 86,010, Deaths: 5,797
Cape Cod: 1,150, Deaths: 93
Texas: 45,198, Deaths: 1,272
New York: 364,745, Deaths: 28,900
New Jersey: 146,334, Deaths: 10,356
Connecticut: 78,839, Deaths: 3,261
Michigan: 51,054, Deaths: 4,891
Illinois: 94,191, Deaths: 4,177
Pennsylvania: 60,622, Deaths: 4,342
Ohio: 26,954, Deaths: 1,581
California: 78,839, Deaths: 3,261

The Dow Jones closed at 24,597.37 on Monday, May 18, 2020.
The FTSE closed at 6,048.59 on Monday, May 18, 2020.

Later today, I will watch the NACAR race. I do not usually watch NASCAR, but today, I will make an exception, and probably enjoy it immensely. This is a return to sports for the nation where we can tune in to where the race will be held without fans at the Darlington Raceway in South Carolina. It is said that it is a 400-mile race, which seems like nothing when compared to the race humanity has endured over the past few months, but we are starving for normality.

I am ending this first account at this stage, looking out at the summer months ahead where the content for the next account to be maintained looks uncertain. At this stage, I do anticipate that the numbers will rise again as we reopen the country, but I also believe it is possible by paying attention to and respecting the "new normal" to keep what Governor Cuomo refers to as "the beast" relatively under control, maintaining the guidelines listed by the President and the CDC. I try to prepare my patients and all others that the numbers of those infected will probably go up, just as the numbers of those recovering will go up, with the number of deaths hopefully being curtailed to a manageable number, fully recognizing that even one death is far too many. However, and as previously stated, I try to instill perspective, resilience, and hope. I also note that many of those with whom I speak still feel that reopening the country marks the end of the virus, and perhaps that is why I am confronted with an increasing number who refuse to wear their masks properly. My response is always the same, cautioning that this is not the end. This is merely the end of the beginning.

So, I am heading out to replenish my groceries and perishables, such as lettuce.

RESET

Afterwards, Mia will take me out for a walk to find her North-South Pooping Axis, after which I will participate in my first NASCAR race, from a safe distance. Mia and Missie will join me. One has a bone; the other has a fluffy toy. As for me, I have…the new and emerging normal.

PERSPECTIVE

"The death of even one is too many, but the unnecessary death of any due to selfishness and stupidity is an insult to our humanity."

– Cheryl Powell

144

CHAPTER 20
Epilogue

As I have indicated in the first account, it is my personal opinion as an observer, participant, and also as a mental health practitioner who is worried about the mental health of our nation, that this virus will run its course. Each time I venture out, I am confronted with people who refuse to wear their masks. I last went for groceries six days ago after closing the first account. Several of the cashiers and baggers wore no masks at all, and the young woman who was attending to my groceries on this occasion had her mask under her nose. I confronted her, politely, and only after expressing my appreciation for her working during the pandemic. Her snappish reply was that, "I'm only told that I have to wear it." Sadly, several of the customers also wore no masks, and this is three months into this ordeal.

On television, as in reality, the protests to end the stay-at-home orders continue, where it is seen that masks and social distancing are also missing, with tensions and anger rising. People are becoming desperate. Others are simply restless as their fears for their health and finances have been left alone like water left boiling in a kettle far too long.

My office at home looks out over a lake where whilst writing this epilogue today, I see a small pontoon boat where I count nine inside. They look to be in their late teens or early 20s, drinking, smoking, radio loud, having a great time – while being roughly one to two feet apart, playfully pushing one another, guys rough-necking...so much for social distancing. I do not begrudge them their fun, but I fear for their safety. Earlier on in this pandemic, I was speaking to those who were attending COVID Parties. We have already seen street parties where the participants have made it clear that they want nothing further to do with the stay-at-home orders and social distancing.

The beaches were opened in Florida and California, and I believe also in Texas, and then needed to be closed again. I suspect this will continue throughout the summer with the beaches opening, people becoming lax, closing them again, then reopening, etc. That is why I do not believe reclosing the country

Cheryl Powell

will work a second time, as we already have large gatherings of protests, other large gatherings, and those ignoring the guidelines – despite the known consequences, further feeding the anxieties, feeding the virus. And then there is the other factor – this is an election year.

One of the good things that arose from this stay-at-home, or what I call "isolation- at-home," is that it seems to have been good for our planet. From across the globe there are observations of clearer skies and a decrease in pollution. Several cities, towns, and countries are also reporting a decrease in their crime rates, which I intend to elaborate on more in a later version as it pertains to reopening, and my suspicion that crime will escalate substantially as we now have many who have been isolated three months, with their anxieties and frustrations left to boil. Our abnormal became the normal, but what about the return to the normal? What lessons will we bring into the new abnormally normal?

I occasionally think back to those two individuals who, long before this pandemic erupted, spoke of a looming doom, a sense of their lives being threatened, a sense of ending. I then think of my own sense, not as desperate, yet enough to prompt me to make initial preparations. Is there something still innate in our humanity that we choose to usually dismiss?

My prediction is still that the numbers of infected, and deaths, will go up again, but hopefully, I pray, not at the rate we encountered only months ago because it is my hope that enough people are now taking the social distancing, hand-washing, and all other guidelines, seriously. It was always my belief that it was the speed at which this virus struck that made it so terrible – like a freight train on steroids and without breaks. There was so little time to prepare, and precious little warning. It has cost too much, and I question what we will discover when all the data is tallied, which I predict will take years, if not decades. How many died from the virus? How many perished, or died earlier from serious delays in receiving their dialysis, radiation, or chemotherapy? How many died from simply being too afraid of going to the hospital? How many were lost because this was an election year? How many suicides? How many died from the cure? And how many will perish not only from this pandemic, but also in the future if we have failed to learn from our history?

PERSPECTIVE

FINAL TRIBUTE

Once again, I would like to thank the media for keeping us informed, thank President Trump, his administration and task force for their ongoing efforts to challenge this spread, and thank the governors who also kept us informed and advised. Despite the fact that I am not always in agreement with our government, as is my right as an American, I recognize that these particular administrations (federal and state) have been confronted with a heavy burden of the magnitude not seen since the last world war. There will always be those who are quick to criticize, but one must also praise tireless efforts.

As mentioned earlier in this account, I would often issue a challenge to my children: not to criticize unless you can propose a better solution. At least at the time of finalizing this first account, it is my personal opinion that there are very few who could have done better, or reacted more swiftly, than those we had leading the battle during this crisis, at least up to the End of the Beginning of Pandemic 2020.

"If you lose hope, somehow you lose the vitality that keeps moving, you lose that courage to be, that quality that helps you go on in spite of it all. And so today I still have a dream."

– Martin Luther King Jr.

"I don't think of all the misery, but of the beauty that still remains."

– Anne Frank

REFERENCES

Agence France-Presse, (February 17, 2020), "Coronavirus: 99 More Cases on Diamond Princess Cruise Ship in Japan as US evacuates citizens." *South China Morning Post.*

American Psychiatric Association. *Diagnostic and Statistical Manual of Mental Disorders. 5th ed.* Arlington, VA: American Psychiatric Association; 2013. [Reference list]. Source: APA, 2013a, pp. 265–290.

Andrzejewski, Adam (March 26, 2020),"Is There Wasteful Spending In The Coronavirus Stimulus Bill?" *Forbes/Open the Books Every Dime Online. In Real Time.*

Anthopolos R, James SA, Gelfand AE, Miranda ML. (June 30, 2011). "A spatial measure of neighborhood level racial isolation applied to low birthweight, preterm birth, and birthweight in North Carolina." *Spat Spatio-Temporal Epidemiol* 2011;2(4):235–46.

Arango, Tim, Fuller, Thomas (May 4, 2020). "Why Liberal Californians Don't Want to Go Back to Normal." *New York Times.*

Bartel AP, Kim S, Nam J, Rossin-Slater M, Ruhm C, Waldfogel J. (January 2019) "Racial and ethnic disparities in access to and use of paid family and medical leave: evidence from four nationally representative datasets." Monthly Labor Review, U.S. Bureau of Labor Statistics, January 2019. hppts://doi.org/10.21916/mlr.2019.2

Berchick ER, Barnett JC, Upton RD. Health Insurance Coverage in the United States: 2018. Current Population Reports, P60-267(RV). U.S. Government Printing Office (Washington, DC) November 2019.

Bravo MA, Anthopolos R, Kimbro RT, Miranda ML. "Residential racial isolation and spatial patterning of type 2 diabetes mellitus in Durham, North Carolina." *Am J Epidemiol* 2018;187(7):1467–7.

Bolin, Bob, and Liza C. Kurtz. "Race, class, ethnicity, and disaster vulnerability." Handbook of disaster research. Springer, Cham, 2018. 181-203.

Brady, JS. (April 23, 2020), "Remarks by President Trump, Vice President Pence, and Members of the Coronavirus Task Force in Press Briefing." *White House Press Briefing Room.*

Brown, Mark, Collett, Gemma, Josland, Elizabeth, Foote, Celine, Li, Quiang.

Brennan, Frank, (February 6, 2015). 10 (2). "Elderly Patients Managed without Dialysis: Survival, Symptoms, and Quality of Life." CJASN.

CDC release (March 28, 2020). "CDC Issues Domestic Travel Advisory for New York, New Jersey, and Connecticut."

CDC release (April 27, 2020). "Loneliness and Social Isolation Linked to Serious Health Conditions."

CDC Release (April 22, 2020). "COVID-19 in Racial and Ethnic Minority Groups CDCv.2019-ncov, racial-ethnic-minorities." https://cdc.gov.coronavirus.

Council of Economic Advisors (May 3, 2019). Unemployment Rate Falls to Lowest Level in Nearly 50 Years; U.S. Economy Adds 263,000 New Jobs in April. https://www.hwitehouse.gov/articles/unemployment-rate-falls

Cunningham, T. J., Croft, J. B., Liu, Y., Lu, H., Eke, P. I., & Giles, W. H. (2017). "Vital signs: racial disparities in age-specific mortality among blacks or African Americans—United States, 1999-2015." MMWR. Morbidity and mortality weekly report, 66(17), 444.

Daley, Brian J, MD, MBA, FACS, FCCP, CNSC; Chief Editor: Praveen K Roy, MD, July 23, 2019, "What is the Prognosis of Tertiary Peritonitis?" *Medscape.*

Dash N. Race and Ethnicity. In: Thomas DSK, Phillips BD, Lovekamp WE, Fothergill A. editors. *Social Vulnerability to Disasters.* 2nd ed. Boca Raton (FL): CRC Press, Taylor & Francis Group. 2013. P. 113-128.

Davenport, Coral, Friedman, Lisa. (January 1, 2020). "Science Panel Staffed With Trump Appointees Says E.P.A. Rollbacks Lackk Scientific Rigor." *Source: Inside Climate News. www.New York Times.com 2019/12/31 epa-science.*

Eder, Steve, Fountain, Henry, Keller, Michael, Xiao, Muyi, Stevenson, Alexandra. "430,000 People Have Traveled From China to U.S. Since Coronavirus Surfaced." *New York Times.* April 4, 2020.

Efrati, I., Rabinowitz, A. (April 20, 2020)."Israel Reverses Trend: More Coronavirus Recoveries Than New cases." *Haaretz News.*

Frank, T.A. November 14, 2016, "Will Trump Be Impeached?" *Vanity Fair/HIVE.*

Fothergill A, Maestas EG, Darlington JD. Race. "Ethnicity and disasters in the United States: A review of the literature." Disasters. 1999; 23(2): 156-173.

Gilead Sciences. April 10, 2020. "Data on 53 Patients Treated With Investigational Antiviral Remdesivir Through the Compassionate Use Program Published in the New England Journal of Medicine." *www.gilead.com › press-room › press-releases › data-o*

Goyal K., Chauhan P., Chhikara K., Gupta P., Singh M.P. (February 27, 2020). "Fear of COVID 2019: first suicidal case in India!" A*sian Journal of Psychiatry.* 2020;49:101989. doi: 10.1016/j.ajp.2020.101989.

Grein, J. MD, Ohmagari, Norio, MD, Ph.D, Shin, D, MD, Diaz, G, MD, Asperges, E, MD, Castagna, A. MD, Feldt, T. MD, Green, M, MD, M.P.H., Gren, G, MD, Lescure, F.X., MD, Ph.D, Nicastri, E., MD, Oda, R, MD. Et.al. June 11, 2020. "Compassionate Use of Remdesivir for Patients with Severe Covid-19." *www.nejm.org › doi › full › 10.1056 › NEJMoa2007016. New England Journal of Medicine.*

Hall, W. J., Chapman, M. V., Lee, K. M., Merino, Y. M., Thomas, T. , Payne, B. K., Eng, E., Day, S. H., & Coyne-Beasley, T. (2015). "Implicit Racial/Ethnic Bias Among Health Care Professionals and Its Influence on Health Care Outcomes: A Systematic Review." *American Journal of Public Health, 105*(12), e60–e76. https://doi.org/10.2105/AJPH.2015.302903.

Hand, Eric, AAAS Science, from Brain & Behavior, Engineering, Technology. Doi:10.1126/science.aaf5803, Research from Joe Kirschvink from the California Institute of Technology.

Hanna, Jason, Moon, Sarah, Chan, Stella. (April 22, 2020). "2 Californians Died of Coronavirus Weeks Before Previously Known 1st US Death." CNN.

Hart, V., Nováková, P., Malkemper, E.P. et al. "Dogs are sensitive to small variations of the Earth's magnetic field." *Frontiers of Zoology* 10, 80 (2013). https://doi.org/10.1186/1742-9994-10-80.

Hearst MO, Oakes JM, Johnson PJ. "The effect of racial residential segregation on black infant mortality." *Am J Epidemiol 2008;*168(11):1247-54.

Higgins-Dunn, Breuninger, K., Kim, J. (April 23, 2020). "New York antibody study estimates 13.9% of residents have the coronavirus, Gov. Cuomo says." *CNBC/Health and Science.*

Hotez, Peter MD, PhD. (March 6, 2020) Dean at the School of Tropical Medicine at Baylor College of Medicine, addressing Congress. CNN.

Jackson SA, Anderson RT, Johnson NJ, Sorlie PD. "The relation of residential segregation to all-cause mortality: a study in black and white." *Am J Public Health* 2000;90(4):615–7.

Jabr, Ferris, March 13, 2020. "Why Soap Works: At the molecular level, soap breaks things apart. At the level of society, it helps hold everything together." New York Times: Health.

Jester, Barbara J. RN.MSN, Uyeki, Timothy M. MD, MPH, MPP, Jernigan, Daniel B. MD, MPH. (May 2020). "Fifty Years of Influenza A (H3N2) Following the Pandemic of 1968." AJPH, *American Journal of Public Health.*

Kang L., Ma S., Chen M., Yang J., Wang Y., Li R. (March 30, 2020). "Impact on mental health and perceptions of psychological care among medical and nursing staff in Wuhan during the 2019 novel coronavirus disease outbreak: a cross-sectional study." Brain, Behavior and Immunity. 2020 doi: 10.1016/j.bbi.2020.03.028.

Kwok, YL, Gralton, J, and McLaws, ML, February 2015. "Face Touching: a Frequent Habit That Has Implications for Hand Hygiene." AM Infect Control, 2015 Feb;43(2):112-4.doi: 10.1016/j.ajic.2014.10.015. *New York Times.*

Loftquist D. Multigenerational Households: 2009-2011. Current Population Reports, P60-267(RV), (Washington, DC) 2012.

Maragakis, Lisa Lockerd, MD, M.P.H. "Coronavirus Disease 2019 vs. the Flu." Johns Hopkins Medicine. www.opkinsmedicine.org.

Montemurro, Nicola (March 30, 2020). "The Emotional Impact of COVID-19: From Medical Staff to Common People." DOI: 10.1016/j.bbi.2020.03.32.

Mnuchen, Steven (April 8, 2020). CNBS Transcript: Treasury Secretary Steven Mnuchen Speaks with CNBCs Jim Cramer on 'Squak on the Street' Todau. CNBC.

National Academies of Sciences, Engineering, and Medicine. 2020. *Social Isolation and Loneliness in Older Adults: Opportunities for the Health Care System.* Washington, DC: The National Academies Press. https://doi.org/10.17226/25663external icon.

Nedelman, Michael, January 23, 2020, "World Health Organization: Wuhan Coronavirus is not yet a Public Health Emergency of International Concern." CNN Health.

NFL News (April 2, 2020). "Patriots' Plane Transports 1.2 Million Masks from China." NFL.com.

Holcombe, Madeline, Shoichet, Catherine (April 16, 2020). "Why California is Giving its own Stimulus Checks to Undocumented Immigrants." CNN.

NIH, National Cancer Institute. February 26, 2016. "Missed Radiation Therapy Sessions Increase Risk of Cancer Recurrence." NIH Staff.

"NYC Health: Sex and Coronavirus Disease 2019 (COVID-19)." REF: The NYC Health Department may change recommendations as the situation evolves. 3.27.20.

New York Times. (Daily). *www.NYTimes.com/interactive/coronavirus-us-cases.*

Perez, E., Sciutto, J., Tapper, J., Bernstein, C.(January 12, 2017). "Intel Chiefs Presented Trump With Claims of Russian Efforts to Compromise Him." *CNN/Politics - online, cnn.com.*

Pierce, Shanley. (November 2, 2019). "Isolation Can Affect the Overall Health of Seniors." Texas Medical Center.

Powell, Jerome, Chair (March 15, 2020). Transcript of Chair Powell's Press Conference Call ... colleagues at the Federal Reserve.

"PTSD Facts & Treatment/Anxiety and Depression Association/ADAA." *Adaa.org/posttraumatic-stress.disorder-ptsd/treatment*

Reger M.A., Stanley I.H., Joiner T.E. (April 10, 2020). "Suicide Mortality and Coronavirus Disease 2019 - A perfect storm?" *JAMA.* Psychiatry. 2020 doi: 10.1001/jamapsychiatry.2020.1060.

Reiche EM, Nunes SO, Morimoto HK. "Stress, depression, the immune system, and cancer." Lancet Oncol. 2004;5:617–625.

Russian Direct Investment Fund (RDIF). (May 13, 2020). "RDIF and Chem-Rar Announce First Interim Results of Clinical Trials of Favipirar Drug's Effectiveness in Coronavirus Therapy." CISION PR Newswire.

Samuelson, Darren, April 17,2016. "Could Trump be Impeached Shortly After He Takes Office?" *Politico Magazine.*

Samuelson, Darren (July 9, 2019). "What's the point? Lawmakers fess up to not fully reading the Mueller report." Politico. Retrieved July 10, 2019.

Smith, Kimberly (March 16, 2020). "Social Isolation Is Linked to Higher Levels of Inflammation." *The Conversation*.

Steenhuysen, Julie (May 14, 2020). "Oxford Coronavirus Vaccine Found Protective in Small Monkey Study." *Reuters*.

Stobbe, Mike. (September 26, 2018). "80,000 People Died of Flu Last Winter in US." *Associated Press*.

Stobbe, Mike (April 8, 2020). "Some Doctors Moving Away from Ventilators for Virus Patients." Associated Press.

Tucker, Jeffrey A. (May 1, 2020)."Woodstock Occurred in the Middle of a Pandemic," *AIER, American Institute for Economic Research*.

Tumilty, Karen (March 27). "Why the Kennedy Center Got Money in the Bailout Bill." *Washington Post*.

Tappe, Anneken, March 23, 2020. "Stocks Close in the Red Despite Fed's Rescue Efforts": March 23, 2020. CNN Business.

Thomas, D.S., Phillips, B.D., Lovekamp, W.E. and Fothergill, A., 2013. "Social vulnerability to disasters." *CRC Press*.

Thucydides – Greek historian. (sometime between 460-400BC). History of the Peloponnesian War (Translated by Richard Crawley). *Dover Publications*.

US Bureau of Labor Statistics, Report 1082, Labor force characteristics by race and ethnicity, 2018. October 2019.
   https://www.bls.gov/opub/reports/race-and-ethnicity/2018/home.htm.

Vikram, Thakur, Anu, Jain (April 23, 2020). "COVID-19 – Suicides: A Global Psychological Pandemic." *Brain, Behavior and Immunity*.

Vogel, K, Mendel, J. (May 1, 2019). "Biden Faces Conflict of Interest Questions That Are Being Promoted by Trump and Allies." *www.New York times/US Politics*.

Weisberger, Mindy. "Mindy quoting Cynthia Otto, Director of Penn Vet's Working Dog Center." Live Science. https://www.livescience.com/dog-smell-covid-19.html

World Health Organization, (March 11, 2019). "WHO Launches New Global Influenza Strategy." *WHO*.

World Health Organization. "Up to 650 000 people die of respiratory diseases linked to seasonal flu each year." *Available: http://www.who.int/mediacentre/news/releases/2017/seasonal-flu/en.*

World Meters. (daily). *www.worldmeters.info/coronavirus. Live Updates.*

Zeitman, Anthony, MD, January 30, 2020. *The International Journal of Radiation Oncology • Biology • Physics. ELSEVIER.*

Also, many thanks to the White House Daily Briefings and press releases, also coverage from news media already mentioned specifically, along with their daily reports sent by e-mail and newscasts in the new normal where a retired journalist might watch objectively to produce this initial account for both the present, and the future – attending from the other side of the screen, observing from an incredibly Safe Distancing – the new Abnormally Normal.